Renowned expert on wo... been a midwife, women's ...... and consultant for the pas...... ..... is internationally active in women's reproductive rights, and is widely sought after for her ability to apply principles of openness and humanism to specific problems.

She has served as a representative to the Midwives Alliance of North America, and is current President of the Midwifery Education Accreditation Council for the United States. She holds a degree in Holistic Maternity Care from Antioch University and is certified by the California Association of Midwives. She lives in Windsor, California and is the mother of three children.

Her previous books include the classic *Heart and Hands: A Midwife's Guide to Pregnancy and Birth*, *Energetic Pregnancy*, and *Women's Intuition*.

Catherine, yo se que
ahora no "stás en vena"
para leer este libro.
No obstante te lo dedico
con mucho amor y
cariño

# WOMEN'S SEXUAL CYCLES

*Understanding your moods and*
*desires at every stage of life*

ELIZABETH DAVIS

Foreword by
GERMAINE GREER

*OPTIMA*

An *Optima* Book

First published in the United Kingdom by Optima in 1994

A CIP catalogue for this book
is available from the British Library

ISBN 0 356 21058 8

Typeset by Solidus (Bristol) Limited
Printed and bound in Great Britain by
Clays Ltd, St. Ives plc

Optima
A Division of
Little, Brown and Company (UK) Limited
Brettenham House
Lancaster Place
London WC2E 7EN

# Contents

# Foreword

## by Germaine Greer

In the post-war years of the twentieth-century, the power of the female stereotype was exponentially extended and intensified by mass marketing, until brassieres and high heels, nail-polish and lipstick were to be found in every hovel on the globe. As its grip tightened, resistance was born. It gathered, swelled, burst through underground channels and up into the consciousness of real women outraged and baffled by the conflicting demands made upon them. The struggle to vomit up the internalised guilts and the ingrained certainties of defect and inadequacy is not over, because male fantasy is still the deciding factor in our buying and selling. The breast-popping stereotype still dangles her four-foot legs off the car hood. The ikon of the dazzling supermenial whose hands never say housework, who is always accessible to the penis and climaxes whenever her partner does (and is never without a desirous partner), and never falters on the rope-bridge over the chasm of parenting, is still displayed in all our houses. But her stranglehold on female variety is gradually being loosened. Gay women have defied her way up front.

Heterosexual women too, have steadily, quietly rewritten the agenda, to include singleness, ageing, aggression, wit and sorrow. Character has been inscribed upon the smooth featureless skin of the stereotype as women have demanded the right to grow up and turn into people.

The great tension at the heart of feminism has always been the pull to demand entry to the male world, and claim an equal share of male characteristics, against the pressure for the right to be different but not inferior. Some feminists argued for the industrialisation of motherhood and the right to carry arms in imperialist wars and to direct the bone-crushing operations of multi-nationals. Others wondered what real femaleness, as distinct from prescribed femininity might be like. They moved into the inscape of the gendered body, deconstructing biological femaleness not as defect, i.e. non-maleness, not as distortion of a male norm by the specific imperatives of child-bearing, but as a complex and variable norm in itself. They took to heart the biological lesson that it is not the female but the male that is the product of a defective gene.

A gifted and persistent group of women professionals set themselves the task of observing at first hand how female humans really do behave. They discovered that all kinds of received ideas about female anatomy were simply wrong, that all kinds of variation were contained within a normality far more capacious than anyone had realised before. Gradually the conviction that femaleness is a permanent disease condition began to lose its hold. Fathers rose from attending birthing women with a new respect for their resilience and power. Women turned away from the hospital and the clinic, looking for ways to take responsibility for their own well-being. Feminist observers put together a picture of a hitherto unknown creature, the well woman.

We still have a long way to go; the medical establishment still labours under the delusion that femaleness is a condition that demands treatment, that women's fertility is the cause of over-population, that machines are better at birthing than women, that wombs are something that should be extirpated, and that the menstrual cycle involves periodic insanity.

Elizabeth Davis has given women the kind of patient, loving and respectful attention that is usually reserved for rhinos and mountain gorillas. Here is a practitioner who does not prescribe but describe, in terms that are both empowering and fascinating, the extraordinary inventiveness and variety of the human female in all her moods and phases.

# Author's note

Another book on sex, you say? What more can be said on the subject? Well, when it comes to sheer technique, or the wily ways of sexual politics, little has been left unsaid. My purpose here, however, is to present a view of women's sexuality that supersedes technique and role-playing, that explores sex from a psycho-physical angle both feminine and feminist.

The need for such a book became clear to me through my work as a midwife, women's health practitioner and health educator. I have been a midwife for 16 years, and have provided well-woman gynaecology and contraceptive care since 1980. I also ran a study through the American Food and Drug Administration on the cervical cap, a newly approved contraceptive device used throughout Europe for many years.

Although it was not the express intent of my research, use of the cervical cap often prompted my subjects to raise issues regarding their sexuality. In fact, many women chose to use the cap because other methods had negative effects on sexual enjoyment. Others found that in using the cap, they became more aware of their anatomy than ever before, and had questions about normal physiological changes during the monthly cycle and how these affect sexual activity. Some of these questions were very basic, and it became clear as I heard them time and again how little even the most sophisticated women may know about hormonal cause and effect when it comes to sexuality. Other issues raised were more involved, regarding fluctuations of desire and emotional responses under a variety of extenuating circumstances. It dawned on me that bits and pieces of information, particularly physical details alone, were not sufficient to meet women's needs. An overview of women's sexuality that incorporated hormonal influences, natural phases of desire during child bearing and rearing, and the effects of the menopause, plus the impact of stress, grief, and relationship upheavals was very much in demand. Thus *Women's Sexual Cycles* was born.

Additional insight and data have been gleaned from my work as a midwife. Many people in this society have the idea that midwives only deliver babies. Not only does our scope of practice include women's general health, but a large measure of patient education and counselling. Pregnancy, birth and postpartum are very vulnerable times for women, times of rapid and often drastic change and adjustment. A woman's relationships with herself, her partner and her close family and friends are brought up for scrutiny: a natural step, really, in preparing for parenthood. But as women feel uncertain in their changing identities, so too their partners may feel displaced, and marriage or family counselling becomes yet another aspect of caring.

Thus I have been privy to the confidences and confessions of hundreds of women in the child bearing cycle. I've also witnessed a fair amount of uninhibited sexual expression and response during labour itself. Although we're taught in this culture that birth is primarily a physical, medical event, in reality it is strongly psycho-sexual. The positions women take, the movements and sounds they make spontaneously in labour (when they feel free and safe enough to do so) are very similar to those in passionate lovemaking. An inextricable part of childbirth preparation is learning to let go completely, to trust one's body, its rhythms and instincts. Naturally, sexual awareness and expression are part of the picture.

Midwives also provide advice on nutrition, exercise, stress reduction, and lifestyle modifications conducive to health. Midwifery care is preventive care, aimed at promoting natural birth. Perhaps a bit of background is in order here: the word midwife comes from Old English and literally means 'with woman'. Midwifery has been a well-established maternity care option in Europe for centuries, but is only now experiencing a resurgence in the United States. In the Netherlands, for example, midwives assist nearly 75 per cent of all births, and over a third take place at home. The safety of midwifery care is demonstrated by the fact that the Dutch have one of the lowest perinatal mortality rates in the world, while the United States ranks a disgraceful 22nd.[1] Largely, this is due to inadequate prenatal care. But now, American women are beginning to seek out midwifery care for the humanistic, personalised approach missing from standard obstetrical care. Midwives see, and treat the *whole woman*, recognising that labour will demand much more than physical preparation as, most surely, will being a parent.

Inevitably, I've carried my midwifery training over to my work in women's health. Thus I've spent many hours listening to women's stories: their fears, concerns, intimate questions, personal triumphs. I've felt deeply satisfied when, after a checkup, a woman tells me she has never had a more comfortable, gentle examination, nor have her questions been answered so thoroughly and respectfully. I feel very grateful for my training and recognise its value. Midwifery has also been a way for me to learn about my own capabilities; as I've learned to trust myself, I've learned to trust women in general. Whenever there is a problem, I believe the woman herself can find the answer, provided she is given adequate information and support. I've discovered that in labour, women often know better than I how to advance the birth. I believe in women's strength and resourcefulness; I've witnessed it time and again. And I also believe that women have been severely short-changed in a culture that defines them as either madonna or whore. Women care about the continuation and continuity of life; they are intrigued by relationships, how things fit together. *Women's Sexual Cycles* is an attempt to honour these attributes of women by presenting an overview wherein the sexual aspect is not separated from everything else.

The first-hand accounts included in the text are both paraphrases of comments made by my clients over the years plus recent interview responses solicited through my women's health practice at Woman-to-Woman Clinic, San Francisco, California. May you be as moved and delighted by the candour of these comments as I have been, and may you draw from them and the women who have shared them, the inspiration to understand, accept and empower yourself!

Elizabeth Davis
Windsor, California 1994

1.  Wagner, Marsden G., 'Infant Mortality in Europe: Implications for the United States', *WHO Journal for Public Policy* (1988)

# 1

# Women, sex and culture

If time and again you have been puzzled by your sexual mood swings, your whims, fantasies and aversions, this book is for you! Women in civilised society have increasingly lost touch with their natural rhythms of sexual desire, particularly in cultures dominated by masculine values and attitudes. Virtually our only popular reference to female sexual rhythms is a negative one, pertaining to the unavailability or undesirability of menstruating women. This is a taboo that we will explore at length later, along with others regarding pregnancy, the menopause and sex in later years. But let us return to the issue at hand: what is the true nature of women's sexuality and women's sexual power?

Before we can even begin to answer this question, we must consider how culture has conditioned us to view sexuality in general. Ours is a black and white society; we're not too fond of shades of grey. The reason for this can be traced to our most fundamental religious ideology, Puritanism. This doctrine sees only good and bad, heaven and hell, God and the Devil, devoid even of the intermediate states (purgatory) and figures (the saints) of

Catholicism and other orthodox religions. This simplistic theology carries over to our social life and institutions. Watch television any night of the week, and you will see good characters and bad ones, with little in between. For years, American movies have featured heroic figures notable for their lack of complexity. This has changed somewhat, particularly with the input of women screenwriters and directors. Nevertheless, to escape our usual two-dimensional reality, we must sift through overt and covert sexual messages that bombard and surround us constantly.

Think about the myths you assimilated in childhood, particularly if you are of the baby-boom generation. Women are virtuous, men are scoundrels. Women don't want sex as much as men do, but they ultimately submit for security's sake. Woman's role is to tame and subdue man, generally by trickery and deceit. Man's role is to take charge, have all the fun and all the say, though laughable and foolish he may be.

Not much of a sexual–social legacy, is it? These suppositions are dehumanising and demeaning to both sexes. They reiterate our cultural dualism, via a definition of sexuality whereby men and women are mutually exclusive opposites. The advertising industry has never stopped sending the message that sex is a battleground. Men win by domination, women, by seduction and submission. Sure, women can have spunk, or a chip on the shoulder now and then, but their power and intelligence must not overshadow men's.

Our social values regarding sex are further expressed by language. Many slang words used to describe the sex act are distinctly unpleasant to women because they portray sex as an act of aggression, male upon female. What's more, these words all imply that sex equals penetration, and thus that the penis and vagina are the primary sex organs. There are few slang words for women's sexual organs anyway, but none in common use for the clitoris. This key source of female sexual pleasure and response is often left undrawn or unlabelled on anatomical sketches; women learn the word clitoris much later than a boy learns the word for his penis. And in sexual activity, male response is the standard against which female response is evaluated and judged. When the penis is suffused with blood, we call it erect, but the clitoris is said to be congested. Even the term vagina comes from the Latin for sheath or scabbard, suggesting a waiting and passive receptacle for the penis. As Sheila Kitzinger, authority on childbirth and women's sexuality, astutely observes, 'language is either silent about women's bodies and sexuality or condemns them'.[1]

And all of this lives on despite the sexual revolution. What was that all about, anyway? Technology was a major factor; the Pill created new possibilities for sexual experimentation and abortion became more readily available. Never before in history had young people dominated the consumer market as they did in the 1960s. Theirs was a generation of optimism, confidence and hope, untainted by memories of war or economic hardship. The sexual revolution seemed promising at first, but in the end, it had very different effects on the sexes. Women had more opportunity to be sexually expressive, but at the same time, they no longer had a legitimate way of saying no. Men, on the other hand, finally had a chance to have sex freely without having to take responsibility. The ultimate effect, in retrospect, was an even greater burden on women and their relationships. Now we know that sex does not necessarily engender intimacy and, if premature or ill advised, may even inhibit normal development. The sexual revolution freed women to have sex according to their passions, but if they chose to avoid it, they were labelled hung-up or even frigid. Social attitudes regarding male superiority and privilege remained the same, so that many women felt more enslaved by their sexuality than liberated to explore its true potential.

Today, when I listen to my daughter's favourite pop songs, I hear messages to the effect that she is expected to 'put out' sexually, and handle the wild and irresponsible behaviour of her man *plus* her own emotional responses. Doesn't sound much like liberation to me! She must also worry about sexually transmitted diseases, pregnancy, and economic dependency should she conceive. No wonder that more women are waiting to become sexually active these days, and are taking the decision to have sex much more seriously.

Underlying the persistent polarisation of the sexes is the disharmony of masculine and feminine energies within us. We all have forceful, aggressive and coolly analytical qualities traditionally considered male, and likewise, vulnerable, sensitive and spontaneous qualities traditionally considered female. As we begin to speak of getting in touch with both sides of ourselves, we must also question what makes men and women uniquely what they are.

In this regard, ground-breaking research began with the Masters and Johnson study in 1966, which revealed for the first time women's orgasmic potential and the importance of clitoral stimulation. Foreplay became a household word, and even though women often feel they don't get enough, at least they don't have to explain what it is to their partners. In fact, some authorities now take exception to the term itself, as it implies that anything short of penetration is merely preliminary and therefore less significant. However, women's need and desire for foreplay can serve as a focal point for closer examination of differences between the sexes. Any woman will tell you that although foreplay is important physically, the emotional aspects of being cared for are even more critical. When foreplay occurs in a spirit of love and tenderness, it enhances physical relaxation and focus. Without the emotional component, foreplay may be little more than an irritation. This brings to mind the classic dichotomy of male/female readiness for intimacy: men need to have sex in order to feel close, women need to feel close in order to have sex.

How much of this is cultural, how much biological? Certainly, as primary caretakers of society and its off-spring, women need support, particularly in caring for the very young. In our society, the trappings of security have traditionally been provided by men. But in other times, in pre-Christian matriarchal cultures, women cared collectively for one another and the children. Although men made important contributions to the system, women did not rely on them for support. These were agrarian societies, based on collective ownership of land and cooperative agricultural efforts. Women were central to these efforts, as well as those of child rearing and education, and depended primarily on the support of other women. Men played secondary roles, relationships were polyandrous, and women did not necessarily know who fathered their children. In fact, in many of these cultures men were not recognised as integral to conception, which was thought to take place by virtue of a woman's relationship with the spirit world. Notably, these were cultures of peace, with shrines and altars everywhere.[2]

Even where hunting was essential, women were origi-nally at the centre of things, clearly recognisable as givers and originators of life. Each person's loyalty was to his or her mother's clan, his or her sister's children. It took many thousands of years for men to perfect weaponry and warfare in order to challenge the creative powers of the mothers.[3] Eventually, they exerted dominance over women as they did over one another. In the face of physical aggression, women soon became dependent on men for survival, and were treated as little more than personal property. Even their innate capacity to heal by way of nature was usurped in favour of tools, instruments, technology. Women who persisted in their power up to medieval times, particularly as healers and midwives, were tortured and burned, in great numbers, at the stake.[4]

No one really knows what female sexuality was like before cultural oppression, but we can speculate. The missionary position was probably not first choice; perhaps women straddled their partners, controlling the rate and depth of penetration, generating their own foreplay. According to ancient Tantric tradition (one highly reverent of women), the posture of choice was entwined sitting, which allowed a slow steady build-up of passion that could at the same time be controlled and maintained.

In any case, today we have a complex situation where traditional male dominance has been challenged by social upheaval. Women who were once expected to stay at home and care for their families have moved fully into the workforce, and many have been disillusioned by the stress and strain of trying to juggle multiple roles of mother, lover, homemaker and executive. Unfortunately, our society has adjusted to the two-income family, so that giving up work or cutting back hours may be economically impossible for many couples. It would seem that women are once again trapped, doomed to over work and/or dependency on men.

Except that men, too, are eager for change. This is the new generation of fathers who have comforted crying babies in the night, changed nappies and altered their work schedules to take care of sick children. Having done so, these fathers have found the fast track not so glittery and far from gold, and many of them want to jump off. Recently, a major American newspaper ran results of a poll indicating that, given the choice, nearly 70 per cent of women and 40 per cent of men would cut back work hours to spend more time with their families. Woven into all of this is an increased awareness of the life cycle, ebb and flow patterns of rest and productivity, emotional ups and downs, creative spurts and periods of dormancy. Despite media messages to the contrary, neither women nor men are always active, nor should they try to be. It is no accident that our society is plagued with stress-related illnesses such as heart disease, high blood pressure, and eating disorders. The need for passing reflection, time-off to appreciate life and one's own unique purpose, now touches both sexes.

How does all of this relate to sexuality? It is increasingly clear that sexual mores too are in upheaval, that the stereotypical roles of man as the aggressive provider and woman as the passive caretaker are outmoded. As new definitions of male and female needs and desires are forged in the United States, even the most entrenched and repressive cultures of the Middle East feel the winds of change. The European view of sexuality has long been unique for its incorporation of sensuality and emotionality, while at the same time maintaining a strict double standard. This, too, is changing.

I recently saw a pregnancy and birth video produced in the Netherlands, and was struck by the unusual opening sequence. This was actually a prolonged shot of a couple cuddling in bed in the morning, he with his eyes closed, a smile on his face, she talking a bit and nuzzling against his cheek. But this was not an afterglow scene, it was the tender moment when she first broke the news that she was pregnant. What struck me most was that here were two equals, vulnerable and strong, sensitive, in touch with themselves, relaxed and communicative. To her news he responded positively, maturely, with none of that feigned idiot shock the American male usually expresses upon hearing that he is going to be a father. This may be due in large part to the fact that Holland provides both maternity and paternity leave, home nursing and housekeeping care after the baby comes and generous support, both social and financial, for the developing family.

Traditionally, the European view of extramarital sex has also been much more liberal than the American attitude. Again, we may look to Puritanical mores, the duality of mind and body (mind is good, body is bad), as causing sex with anyone but sanctioned spouse to be riddled with guilt and confusion. Apart from the general controversy on the subject, pornography in America must be noted for its unusual violence and brutality. When people are taught to mistrust their bodies and feelings, it's no wonder that their sexual imagery reflects that violation.

We can trace this alienation back to the Garden of Eden myth, wherein Eve made the grievous mistake of commingling with the serpent. New Age interpretations of this story see the serpent as Kundalini, or the vital power that may be awakened by uniting one's physical, sexual self with higher intelligence. My favourite T-shirt logo sums it up very nicely: 'Eve Chose Consciousness'. But Christianity categorically maintains that to seek enlightenment through the body is tantamount to sin. What does this mean for women, who have no choice but to unite with their bodies in birth, or suffer? What does this mean for all of us but isolation, disease and neurosis? To quote Susan Griffin:

Consciousness and meaning are part of nature. . . . When bodily knowledge and language are separated, we ourselves experience a terrible separation which ranges all the way from grief to despair to madness. . . . In this way culture destroys a woman's conscious knowledge of her own experience. Just as she is separated from other women, from her body and her feelings, she is, finally, a stranger to herself.[5]

Fortunately, we've countered with feminism, at first intensely political but more recently humanistic, even spiritual. Against all odds, women are rediscovering their natural strengths, their unique abilities and propensities apart from men. They are pulling together in groups, purging themselves of mistrust and competitiveness. They are formulating communications systems according to need, devising social structures to support them in various life phases, reanimating ritual celebrations and acknowledgements from the past, or inventing new ones to suit the present. The new feminism, highly personal hence imminently practical, has evolved from our need to unite mind and body, to reclaim the psycho-sexual events of menstruation, childbirth, breastfeeding and the menopause as self-affirming and significant, rather than sinful or unclean, to derive power from being *female*.

Beyond simply acknowledging that our sexuality depends on our moods, and that these fluctuate according to hormonal, biological and social influences, lies the potential to work with our rhythms instead of against them, to stop denying the ebb and flow patterns of existence and start using them to enhance the quality of our lives, not only for ourselves but for our loved ones, our culture, our world. It might well be said that to do so is crucial to our very survival. To my mind, woman's reunion with her body is a metaphor for healing the planet, saving the earth.

Accordingly, we must expand our definition of sexuality to reflect the interrelatedness of all life. We are accustomed to thinking of sexuality in the most limited way, as the physical act of intercourse alone. A more meaningful and pertinent definition is so broad as to be nearly unrecognisable: for a woman, sexuality is all that it means to be female. This may include physical, erotic expression, but it definitely involves the relationship of our vital energies to all aspects of existence. Actually, Webster's definition is not far off the mark: 'The sum of structural, functional and behavioral peculiarities of living beings that subserve reproduction and distinguish males from females.'[6]

Apart from cultural influences, then, are there behavioural differences between the sexes that can be linked to basic biology? While researching *Women's Intuition*,[7] I found that certain gender specific characteristics reveal themselves early in infancy, long before acculturation takes place. For example, baby boys demonstrate a much stronger attraction towards tangible objects than do girls. Girls are more interested in the human face, in communication. Whereas men can see better in bright light and at a distance, women literally see the big picture: they have wider peripheral vision due to extra rods and cones at the back of the retina. And when it comes to tactile sensitivity, even the least sensitive woman is more sensitive than the most sensitive man (this is one test area where scores of each sex don't even overlap!)[8]

Beyond the unique aptitudes of each sex, research shows that the brains of men and women are actually structured differently. This is new information for the general public, but old news to the neuroscientists. In an era of professed sexual equality, these findings have been considered so radical and subversive that grant monies for further research have been repeatedly denied for fear that results might be used to argue for male superiority. But the current debate among leading female thinkers underscores the need for this information.

In her book, *Backlash: The Undeclared War Against American Women*, Susan Faludi documents the myriad ways in which data has been misrepresented to undermine and subvert women's gains of the 1970s and 1980s, perpetuating, to some extent, feminism which sees men as the problem or at the very least calls for a change in male values and behaviour. Camille Paglia, controversial author of *Sexual Personae*, finds this sort of feminism self-indulgent and simplistic, loaded with unrealistic expectations of what men must do in order for women to find true equality. 'Women will never know who they are until they let men be men,'[9] she tells us, at the same time deriding feminists as snivelling, whiny women who ought just to get on with their lives. But she fails to place feminism in socio-historical context, to honour its accomplishments and forgive its excesses. Beyond this polarisation, I believe the promise of female autonomy may be found in embracing the achievements of our past, as we work for a future where women can really be women. Men are not the target, though culture may be to some degree, or perhaps we are just beginning to see how truly separate and different are the basic natures of each sex.

To return to the research: we now know that the foetus itself produces hormones around six weeks gestation which differentiate the sex organs and further affect brain development. The male cortex thickens on the right side, the female, on the left. The cortex contains key control centres that govern behaviour; in the male functions are highly specialised according to hemisphere, but in the female functions are diffused, replicated on both left and right sides of the brain. An outstanding example regards the emotional centres, which in women are located in both hemispheres but in men are found on the right side only. Add to the picture the fact that men have verbal centres only in the left hemisphere, and we see a biological basis for the difficulty men have in expressing their feelings.[10]

Due to a thickening of the corpus callosum (the part of the brain that connects the two hemispheres), women also show a much greater ability to switch back and forth between hemispheres. This may explain the female ability to coordinate several activities simultaneously, whereas males prefer to concentrate on one thing at a time. Women's attention is generally more diffused; their approach to problem-solving is to encircle, consider the problem from a variety of angles and then come to a conclusion. Men tend to be intensely focused in their problem-solving, building in factors bricklayer-style, somewhat methodically. This is why, when the two sexes solve problems together, men are at a loss to understand why women bring in so many seemingly unrelated subjects and don't get to the point, while women wonder what's wrong with figuring things out by thorough discussion. Women by nature tend to expand, while men contract.

We can readily extrapolate these characteristics to differing sexual styles. John Gray, Ph.D., author of *Men, Women and Relationships*, notes that widespread misunderstanding of basic differences between the sexes is at the root of most sexual dissatisfaction and dysfunction. What then does a woman need from a lover? Assistance in focusing, in bringing her diffused and expanded awareness (especially after a busy day) to focus on herself, her body and sexual pleasure. It has been shown that women need an average of eighteen minutes' stimulation to reach orgasm, whereas men need only two or three. Women need cuddling, they need to be held and touched in a non-sexual way at first, erogenous zones aside. As Gray astutely observes, the delicious, total-body pleasure a woman feels from this warm-up is much like what a man feels *after* his climax. He will increasingly focus and contract his sexual tension until he ejaculates. Women and men can help each other by recognising and balancing their differences; he, by taking the time to help his partner relax, she, by making the wait enjoyable for him or by being up for an occasional 'quickie'.

But apart from men, and from sex, women have their own inherent mechanisms for focus and balance: biological rhythms. The monthly cycle, for example, moves a woman through a definite set of psychological stages that come full circle. Each time round, she experiences a full spectrum of emotional reactions and opportunities for self-expression. There is return and repetition but with continued growth, in a pattern resembling a spiral. Biological rhythms give women's lives meaning, they are vehicles for transformation. Every time a woman nears menstruation it is likely she will reflect on emotional difficulties and dissatisfactions in her life and have another go at their resolution. Menstruation occurs generally by lunar month, so that women are naturally tied to cosmic rhythms that profoundly influence existence.

Yet all of this may be negatively affected by the concept of woman as nurturer. Although this capability is to some degree biologically programmed, it has nonetheless been exploited by society. Remember that in a patriarchal system such as ours, woman as man's subordinate is responsible to him before herself. Despite clear evidence of hormonal and physiological factors in maternal instinct and behaviour, there is no indication that this applies to the care of grown men, let alone those outside one's immediate family. And yet, for many generations women have been made to live their lives through others. Their worth has been assessed on the basis of how well they've fostered male 'superiors': 'Behind every good man there's a good woman.' If or when the family falters, the guilt and blame invariably falls on the woman. She is responsible for discerning problems, implementing solutions, and coordinating everything to bring about ultimate harmony. She is generally so busy with these truly formidable tasks that she has little time for herself. Long suffering, self-sacrificing, stoic, faithful, complacent in face of life's 'realities', yet willing and able to fight fiercely to defend her kin: this is a laughable image to many of us today, yet the basic social pattern persists.

As we nurture others to the exclusion of ourselves, it follows that we'll attempt to live out our dreams and fantasies through them as well. As the contemporary saying goes, 'Women marry hoping to change their partners; men marry hoping their partners will never change.' We must, once and for all, see this for what it is: a recipe for loss and disappointment. Only by asserting ourselves, establishing our own needs and finding ways to meet them can we hope to find fulfilment in life. Although we may want to nurture and care for others to a certain extent, let it be by choice rather than by obligation.

All things considered, it's hardly surprising that although women today are better educated and more socially sophisticated than at any time in recent history, we remain puzzled by and at the mercy of our hormonal and biological rhythms, unable to incorporate these successfully into our lives. This is largely because, as was stated earlier, our rhythmic energies engender an ebb and flow approach to living distinctly at odds with the masculine 'ladder of success' model. But now perhaps we can begin to share with our partners and society a fuller definition of what it means to be a woman, and the lessons we've learned that have yet to be generally acknowledged. These are the things women know: that everything comes around, that reflection is germane to creative action, and that the passage of time alone can be a key factor in change. We've learned these things organically, through the monthly cycle, in gestating young, in weathering the phases of child bearing and child rearing, in transforming through the menopause. As society cries out for balance, for genuine solutions to overemphasis of the masculine, the unchecked pursuits of war and aggression at the cost of social services and education, women's wisdom is once again coming to the fore. Women are speaking out and being heard.

1. Kitzinger, Sheila, *Woman's Experience of Sex* (New York, Penguin Books, 1985)
2. Iglehart, Hallie, *Woman Spirit* (San Francisco, Harper & Row, 1983)
3. Walker, Barbara, *The Crone* (San Francisco, Harper & Row, 1985)
4. Ehrenreich, Barbara and English, Deidre, *Witches, Midwives and Nurses: A History of Women Healers* (New York, Feminist Press, 1973)
5. Griffin, Susan, *Pornography and Silence* (New York, Harper & Row, 1981)
6. Merriam Co., G & C, *Webster's New Collegiate Dictionary* (Chicago, R.R. Donnelley and Sons, 1969)
7. Davis, Elizabeth, *Women's Intuition*, (Berkeley, California, Celestial Arts, 1990)
8. Moir, Anne and Jessel, David, *Brain Sex* (New York, Carol Publishing Group, 1991)
9. Paglia, Camille, 'Hurricane Camille Wreaks Havoc', *San Francisco Chronicle* (September 1992)
10. Moir and Jessel, *Brain Sex*

# 2

# Hormonal influences

When I was in my early twenties, I remember wondering why female animals went into heat while we women apparently did not. How could something so nearly universal in the animal kingdom (mammalian, at least) be omitted from the most highly evolved species? I was familiar with the theory that women can and will have sex at any time of the month, at any point in the cycle, due to the intellectual aspect of human desire. Yet this was not a fully satisfactory answer, for although it acknowledged the psychological component of women's desire it did not address the physical and hormonal underpinnings, of which I knew virtually nothing.

Later, after the birth of my second child, and after having tried nearly every available method of contraception with varying degrees of dissatisfaction, I decided to learn about fertility awareness. I soon discovered the postpartum period to be one of the most challenging times to make the attempt, as I was still breastfeeding and not yet menstruating, with extreme hormonal fluctuations. Yet, after some months of observation, I began to catch on. Once I re-established my normal cycle, I observed not only the signs and symptoms of my fertility in mucus changes and temperature fluctuations, but the emotional and sexual mood swings that accompanied these. Beyond a doubt, I noticed that my desire for sex was greater when I was fertile. What's more, I exuded a copious vaginal secretion with a definite odour that seemed to put both me and my partner in the mood. Perhaps, I thought to myself, we women have a 'heat' of our own after all!

I recently attended a midwifery conference and one of the few male presenters, a physician, mentioned in passing that according to his patients, the ovulatory phase was the time they felt most like making love. 'How about the *only* time!', one of the women in the audience piped up, and the entire room broke into laughter. A moment of truth, it seems, and in marked contrast to the 'anytime, ever ready' notion.

Let's look at the hormonal changes that occur day-to-day in the monthly cycle, and examine how these influence sexual rhythms and response. But first, we must introduce the key hormones, and consider their specific actions in detail.

### THE HORMONES

We'll start with oestrogen, often considered the quintessential female hormone. It is made by the ovaries, under signals from the pituitary gland, which is further regulated by the hypothalamus.

Oestrogen plays a major role during puberty, causing breast development, changes in sweat glands to produce body odour, changes in the vagina and its secretions, and enlargement of the external genitals (labia and clitoris). In the mature woman, oestrogen triggers ovulation, and during pregnancy is responsible for breast growth, vaginal and cervical changes, and uterine enlargement.

Progesterone is the other key hormone in women's lives. It is also produced by the ovaries, specifically by the disintegrated egg follicle known as the corpus luteum. It too plays a role in the monthly cycle; once ovulation has occurred, progesterone keeps the uterine lining growing and rich enough to nourish the embryo in the event of conception. During pregnancy, it reduces uterine irritability so the uterus will retain its contents, and eventually its manufacture is taken over by the placenta.

Now, let's see how these hormones work in concert during an average cycle of 28 days. As menstruation begins on day one, one of the pituitary hormones, follicle stimulating hormone (FSH), sends a message to the ovaries to start producing oestrogen. Around day five, oestrogen is released into the bloodstream and returns to the pituitary gland. When oestrogen reaches a certain level, the pituitary secretes less FSH and releases another hormone, lutinising hormone (LH).

This brings us to mid-cycle, or day 14. Oestrogen is at its peak, and LH flows to the ovary to stimulate one of the follicles there to ripen and release an egg. The egg bursts from the follicle and is drawn into the Fallopian tube: this is ovulation. Once empty, the follicle becomes the corpus luteum and starts to produce progesterone.

Please refer to the diagram on page 20. Note that oestrogen levels peak mid-month, just as progesterone levels are beginning to rise. Progesterone reaches its peak around day 24 or 25; at this point, if fertilisation has not occurred, LH shuts down, the corpus luteum withers and progesterone levels drop sharply. Meanwhile, oestrogen levels will have gradually reached their lowest point as well; when both have hit bottom, menstruation occurs.

oestrogen

progesterone

LH (lutenising hormone)

FSH (follicle stimulating hormone)

basal body temperature

days 1    menses    14    ovulation    28

## PHYSICAL CHANGES THROUGHOUT THE CYCLE

Now that the technical details are in place, let's consider the signs and signals we women experience at different points in the cycle. Keep in mind that the 28 day cycle is fairly common but far from standard; cycles may run as little as 21 days or more than 40. And fluctuations month-to-month are also normal.

Menstruation itself may last as little as three days or as many as seven. Women with longer periods often have a day in the middle when the flow stops, before a final day or two of bleeding. After menstruation there are usually several days with little or no vaginal secretion, known in the fertility awareness method as dry days. (These are the days when, if you want to make love, you need ample stimulation to lubricate.) Depending on the length of menstruation and the overall length of the cycle, dry days may be numerous or entirely absent. How so? Take a look at the chart on page 24. This shows a comparison of several different women's cycles. Note that regardless of cycle length, ovulation occurs 14 days before menstruation begins. Barring abnormal conditions, this time span is biochemically fixed; room for variation occurs only in the pre-ovulatory phase, where length of menstruation, dry and pre-ovulatory days may be somewhat unpredictable in number.

Pre-ovulatory days are characterised by a build-up of vaginal secretion, which is usually white and creamy. Gradually, this is replaced by a fairly clear, slippery and profuse mucus during the fertile days. Ovulation takes place when the fertile mucus reaches a peak, at which point it has a unique quality known as 'spin' (from the German *spinnbarkeit*), noted when a bit of mucus pressed between the fingertips stretches to form a strand as the fingers are pulled apart. This mucus also has the same alkaline pH as seminal fluid, and the perfect molecular structure for sperm to swim through. It can also keep sperm living in the vagina for a number of days. This is why, when using fertility awareness as a contraceptive method, you must abstain or use protection from the first sign of secretion after dry days. You never know when your mucus will shift to fertile, and as it does, any sperm in the canal or cervical crypts (little pockets within the cervical opening) can be kept viable until the egg is released.

Fertile mucus lasts approximately five to seven days, then shifts abruptly back to a drier, stickier, yellow-white discharge. However, a woman is not safe from pregnancy until three and a half of these post-ovulatory days have passed, allowing time for the more acidic pH of this mucus to kill off any remaining sperm. In a 28 day cycle, this brings us to about day 19 or 20.

The rest of the month is characterised by the same stickier mucus – with one exception. Some women note a release of secretion that closely resembles fertile mucus just before menstruation begins. This is actually a mucus plug from the cervix, developed under the influence of progesterone to protect the uterus from infection; it is shed spontaneously as progesterone levels fall. Now menstruation is set to begin.

An important aside: bear in mind that it takes time, usually at least six months of observation, to know enough about your cycle to be able to use contraception selectively. For example, fertile mucus looks very much like arousal lubrication, and cervical secretions may be severely altered by vaginal infection. You must allow enough time to incorporate such variations in your understanding.

Besides changes in secretion, women also experience fluctuations in breast size, weight, pelvic sensations and body temperature during the cycle. Mid-cycle, breast tenderness and enlargement are due to general water retention, which may also cause a pound or two of weight gain. (As oestrogen levels fall, these effects diminish.) Also noteworthy is the mid-cycle sensation of *mittleschmerz*, which may range from a subtle twinge to a strong cramping feeling as the egg is released from the ovary.

Breast and weight changes later in the cycle are partially due to a second, lesser peak of oestrogen; they are further exaggerated by the presence of progesterone. Progesterone is known as a heat producing hormone, high levels of which may cause a noticeable rise in body temperature. In contrast, when levels plunge premenstrually, women typically experience cold hands and feet.

There are other physiological changes that account for the many premenstrual symptoms. High levels of steroid hormones may cause intestinal cramping or diarrhoea; conversely, some women experience constipation in this phase. Steroids also cause expansion and contraction of blood vessels; as levels fluctuate, women may experience headaches, inflammation of varicose veins or rapid heartbeats.

A common question among women in their mid-thirties is why premenstrual syndrome (PMS) seems to be getting worse, or if never a problem before, noticeable for the first time. As we mature, the mid-cycle oestrogen peak gets higher, while the second rise tends to diminish. Thus progesterone and steroid effects, without the modification of oestrogen, become even more exaggerated.

During menstruation itself, levels of progesterone and oestrogen are at their lowest points (although the pituitary gland is primed to release FSH and set the cycle in motion once more). It is interesting that this hormonal low point is literally a fallow phase, a time free enough of hormonal influences for rest, reflection and rejuvenation naturally to occur.

## EMOTIONAL AND SEXUAL MOOD SWINGS

Perhaps you've already begun to link these physical changes to your own patterns of emotional and sexual response. As menstruation ends and dry days begin, it's no wonder

## Sample Menstrual Cycles

| Average/Long Cycle | | Short Cycle | | Stress-Related Cycle | |
|---|---|---|---|---|---|
| Day | [Discharge] | Day | [Discharge] | Day | [Discharge] |
| 1 | menses | 1 | menses | 1 | menses |
| 2 | menses | 2 | menses | 2 | menses |
| 3 | menses | 3 | menses | 3 | menses |
| 4 | menses | 4 | spotting | 4 | spotting |
| 5 | menses | 5 | menses | 5 | dry |
| 6 | spotting | 6 | menses | 6 | dry |
| 7 | dry | 7 | spotting-slick | 7 | slippery |
| 8 | dry | 8 | slick | 8 | moist |
| 9 | dry | 9 | stretchy | 9 | moist |
| 10 | dry | 10 | dry | 10 | damp |
| 11 | dry | 11 | dry | 11 | dry |
| 12 | dry | 12 | dry | 12 | dry |
| 13 | creamy | 13 | dry | 13 | stretchy |
| 14 | creamy | 14 | dry | 14 | slippery |
| 15 | wet-milky | 15 | dry | 15 | wet |
| 16 | slippery | 16 | dry | 16 | dry |
| 17 | stretchy | 17 | gummy | 17 | dry |
| 18 | dry | 18 | gummy | 18 | dry |
| 19 | gummy | 19 | dry | 19 | pasty |
| 20 | dry | 20 | slippery | 20 | gummy |
| 21 | pasty | 21 | damp | 21 | dry |
| 22 | pasty | 22 | menses | 22 | dry |
| 23 | gummy | | | 23 | dry |
| 24 | dry | | | 24 | dry |
| 25 | dry | | | 25 | dry |
| 26 | dry | | | 26 | dry |
| 27 | dry | | | 27 | dry |
| 28 | damp-spotting | | | 28 | menses |
| 29 | slick | | | | |
| 30 | menses | | | | |

that many women don't feel much like making love. After all, vaginal dryness isn't particularly erotic, and on a purely physical level, the hormonal upswing has just begun. However, many women find the pre-ovulatory phase a great time to make plans and, as oestrogen increases, a great time to get things done.

Accordingly, ovulation is the high point of the month, generally a time of peak performance. A fascinating study cited in a newspaper some years ago showed that women in their fertile phase scored higher on achievement tests than at any other time of the cycle, turning in top performances in athletic competitions, written examinations and intelligence testing![1] The physical components of the fertile phase – elevated body temperature, fullness and sensitivity of the breasts, the slippery wetness of the vagina as though already aroused – often add a dimension of self-confidence, certainly and richness to a woman's personal demeanour. All systems are 'go'; when we're fertile, we're 'on'. And yes, like it or not, we're definitely 'in heat'; were our genitals exposed and visible to potential partners (rather than being wiped dry repeatedly during the day or deodorised with panty-liners), tell-tale signs both visual and olfactory would signal our biological receptivity.

Women who are unaware of the cycle of mucus changes often think they are developing an infection during the fertile phase. It's not that the discharge is offensive, it's just that it's so profuse, and tends, when exposed to air and kept warm (as in underwear), to develop a rather musty odour. One woman graphically described this as a 'barnyard smell': somewhat sweet and strong. As a matter of fact, women's sense of smell is more acute than men's, and around ovulation is especially attuned to a musk-like odour associated with men (the synthetic form of which is called exaltolide). It is a smell most women find quite attractive.

Needless to say, this *is* a great time for lovemaking. As Sharon says, 'It's the time I'm always ready. I don't need foreplay because I'm already wet, but the more I have, the more powerful my orgasm.' The intensity of orgasm can be partially correlated to the oestrogen peak. A unique propensity of this hormone is to stimulate circulation in the pelvic area, including vaginal tissues. These literally become hot and swollen with blood, and the internal muscles are more sensitive and responsive.

Emotionally, women note that they feel decidedly amorous around this time. Sara describes it this way: 'For me, there is both passion and tenderness. I really want Tom, but I don't feel tense or rushed about it. I feel ripe, full, with passion all through me. I feel like playing and taking my time, because I know my body is set for maximum sensation and incredible orgasm.'

Women typically describe orgasms when fertile as 'deep, very deep in my vagina', 'at the core of my being', or 'a total body experience'. One woman went on to say, 'I feel like my whole body, all of me is one giant sexual receptor.' Another states, 'I feel sacred when I'm fertile, like all of me is at its best. I feel integrated, free.'

Mary vividly describes not only her physical response but her emotional tone as, 'Sweet ... it's like waves of warm honey flowing through me.' Another woman notes, 'This is the time when I can really move a tremendous amount of energy through my body. Sometimes, other times when we make love and I come right away, I feel a little let down. But when I'm fertile, there's so much charge I can build it up, spread it out, and keep doing that until my orgasm is a total thing, it just carries me off completely.'

The qualities of 'totality' and 'sweetness' we can link to oestrogen, but the intensity these women describe is at least partially due to a burst of hormones from the adrenals, called androgens. Generally considered male because they stimulate growth of body hair, deepening of the voice and increased muscle mass in men, for women they are relatively insignificant except during ovulation, when they surge. The increase in libido (sex drive) most women feel mid-cycle is thought to be caused primarily by androgens.

This discussion would not be complete without some mention of pheromones, olfactory stimulants released through the perspiration of both men and women. Winnifred B. Cutler made ground-breaking news in 1986 with her discovery that male pheromones could serve to regulate female menstrual cycles. With just a bit of pheromone substance (collected from male sweat samples) placed under their nostrils, 70 per cent of women with highly irregular cycles became regular in a matter of months. Similarly, Martha McClintock demonstrated the menstrual synchrony of women sharing quarters in college dorms, due also to the effects of pheromones (1971). Even more intriguing is the finding that in monogamous couples, sexual rhythms tend to synchronise, with male testosterone surges matching female oestrogen and progesterone, largely in response to pheromone exposure.[2]

And yet, beyond hormonal factors and physical cues there must be, for the intelligent, thinking creatures we women are, an element of desire that springs entirely from the awareness of our fertility and the knowledge that we have the power to conceive. Not necessarily the intent, but the power to recreate ourselves. Listen to what Ellen has to say: 'Just knowing I'm fertile gets me completely turned on. This is the time of the month when I feel the power of creation flowing through me. Once my partner is aware, too, he intensifies my feelings with his own. We use condoms, and sometimes we "play the edges" by having long, drawn-out foreplay, with an element of danger and excitement in being unprotected until we finally get the condom in place. The *charge* we build up, the intimacy, is really something else!'

The flip side of this is the difficulty some couples have in using contraception with this awareness, in the sense that it may feel like a violation or, at the very least, a letdown. Some choose to use fertility awareness as their only method of birth control, and either abstain during ovulation or have sexual activity other than penile/vaginal intercourse.

Particularly if a couple has children already and thus knows the ultimate potential of this time, or if one wants another child while the other does not, the emotional content of sex during this phase can be rather explosive. Ultimately, sex is a vehicle of communication, and as such does not always trigger easy or pleasant revelations.

We'll look more at contraceptive methods and issues later in the chapter; suffice it for now to say that the fertile time is indeed a power point. Apart from sexual activity, some women actually plan key business meetings, important family events, holidays or new ventures to coincide with this phase. From Gina: 'I'd been observing my cycles for a long time, four years maybe, when I finally realised I had more energy and did my best work on the upswing from when my period ended on through ovulation. What's even more interesting is that part of me has incorporated the rhythm of my cycle in day-to-day planning – I don't even have to think about it.'

Does this mean that the post-ovulatory phase is nothing but a downhill slide? Not really, for although oestrogen diminishes, progesterone picks up. Nevertheless, there are other substances released from the adrenals called aldosterones, that apparently have something of an opposite effect to that of the androgens. Thus some women do report less sexual activity immediately after ovulation.

Several days before menstruation, however, when progesterone levels are highest, many women notice a second sexual peak in the cycle. Asked to characterise it, they say, 'hot', 'intense', 'urgent', 'driving', or 'very physical'. Remember that progesterone is heat producing; it is interesting how these sexual metaphors correspond to this quality. Samantha says, 'Right before my period, I feel, I don't know, more masculine in my approach to sex, more aggressive.' And from Joan, 'I want it fast, hot, physically rough ... I come quickly, explosively – it's great!' Ann observes, 'I'm less emotional about sex – really, I just want to get off.'

Mild premenstrual symptoms such as heightened sensitivity of the skin, especially the breasts and nipples, may further increase sexual pleasure. Many women prefer being on top during lovemaking at this time so they can control depth of penetration, the exact angle and rate of clitoral stimulation. Plus, there is more opportunity in this position for being touched and caressed. On the other hand, if premenstrual symptoms are severe, it may be that *any* stimulation will be too much until menstruation is underway.

A few words about PMS in general: one theory is that low progesterone levels could be a cause. This may be your problem particularly if you experience break-through bleeding or spotting several days before your period begins (remember, progesterone's job is to maintain the uterine lining). In fact, I've had increasing numbers of women in my practice reporting this occurrence as periodic or even chronic. It's possible that progesterone levels are low relative to an excessive amount of oestrogen taken through the diet via certain foods. The use of stilboestrol, an oestrogen-like substance, is quite common for fattening beef cattle and for making the meat more tender. However, residues remain and become highly concentrated in milk and milk products. An obvious solution is to minimise consumption of these foods, or look for natural alternatives. Another possibility is acupuncture treatment, which can be used to stimulate the pituitary gland and subsequently the ovaries, to produce oestrogen and progesterone in appropriate amounts.

The use of progesterone by ingestion or vaginal suppository has been randomly successful at best, and may have little more than a placebo effect for conditions other than that cited above. After all, it's the pituitary that masterminds ovarian function; it doesn't make sense that dosing the body with hormones would create any lasting effect. Recent studies have in fact shown that even women with severe PMS generally have normal amounts of oestrogen and progesterone during the cycle. Another theory is that abnormal levels of serotonin in the brain may cause PMS and that the amino acid L-tryptophan may somehow be implicated in alleviating symptoms. L-tryptophan in excessive amounts can be dangerous, but certain foods, such as turkey, have naturally high amounts.

Most women today are also well aware that PMS has its emotional components: moodiness, anger, borderline hysteria. But beyond hormonally induced responses, might there not also be psychological conditions that predispose someone to PMS? I recall a client of mine who was quite concerned that she might be pregnant – she was two weeks late and had never missed a period yet two pregnancy tests came back negative. Several days later she reported this dream: she was in her office, feeling under pressure due to a boom in her business, and her papers began blowing around, all over everywhere when she heard a voice say, 'just let go'. As it turned out, she actually missed a cycle altogether but then resumed her normal rhythm. Admittedly, this example goes beyond mere PMS, but it illustrates psychological conditions that can cause it to become extreme.

This is a theme I explored at length in my last book, *Women's Intuition*: the function of the premenstrual phase on a psychic level as a time for letting go, relinquishing control, allowing the end of one cycle to make way for the next. Before the sorting and re-ordering, dreaming and developing must come the release, the surrender, the death of the old. Consider again the hormonal influences: after progesterone peaks, both it and oestrogen plummet – no gradual dip or decline, but rather, a harrowing fall. Making way for the next cycle means getting out of the way intellectually, bottoming-out, getting down to one's essence. This is the basis of renewal.

Depending on how readily or easily this occurs, sex may or may not seem desirable. As Sandra reports, 'Once I know my period is going to start – I'm cramping or spotting a little – I like to wait on making love until it really gets going. I feel like keeping to myself until I've turned the corner. It's an energy thing for me.' Quite the opposite, Pat reports, 'A day or two before my period – Wow, look out – I've got only one thing on my mind!'

Even if our premenstrual symptoms are relatively mild and consistent, all of us have a terrible time of it now and then. Screaming at our kids, fighting with our loved ones, breaking or throwing things, crying in public places – these extremes are usually the tail end of a very trying, difficult month, or perhaps a period of less than optimal health. Poor health and stress can definitely disrupt the metabolism and affect hormonal balance. Keeping tabs on ourselves day-to-day, not overdoing it, getting enough rest and relaxation all help, but sometimes circumstances go beyond that. Take a look at the box on page 33 for special ways to cope.

And now, one of the most persistent taboos: sex during menstruation. Even as little as five years ago, women were cautioned by physicians that it might lead to infection ('blood is a good culture medium for bacteria'), and many men are still influenced by ancient taboos that depict association with menstruating women as a brush with the dark side. Why so? Well, in biblical times a menstruating woman was considered unclean, as was everything she touched. Under the laws of Moses, sex was strictly forbidden during, and for a week after, the period. Since a woman's primary function at this time was to produce as many children as possible, it's likely her chances were intensified by staying away from her husband for a while so his sperm count could increase, then later reuniting with him right in mid-cycle.

Even in so-called primitive societies, women have long been isolated during menstruation, not for being unclean, but overly powerful and magical. The fact that women could bleed without consequence of illness, debility or death was definitely confounding and frightening to the men of these cultures. However, in the matriarchies of ancient times, the menstrual phase was considered a time of psychic enhancement, a period for unifying earthly and heavenly influences. The connection is clear: many women respond to lunar forces by menstruating regularly on either the full or new moon. Also, before the days of tampons and so-called 'sanitary' towels, women let themselves bleed into the earth, fertilising it and thus feeling powerfully linked to all living things.[3] Women had a sense of significance and connection with nature that many find missing in today's world.

Nevertheless, women of today do report increased sensitivity while menstruating through dreams, symbolic occurrences, and intuitive insights or communications. In her

## WAYS TO COPE WITH PMS

1.  **Evoke your emotions** Listen to the most sentimental, moving music, the kind that hits the spot, and let yourself cry, yell, rave freely. As we midwives say to women postpartum, 'letting the tears flow will let the milk come down'; the same is true of tears and menstruation.

2.  **Experience the dark side** Review the under-belly of the month, all the things that have hurt you, made you blue, made you feel furious or powerless. Be aware of accumulated tensions.

3.  **Note spontaneous resolutions** As you relive the negative events of the cycle, make note of any flashes of resolve, inspirations of ways to do it differently or better. This is a great time for, 'I'm never going to let X happen to me again,' or, 'I'm not going to do Y any more!'

4.  **Eat** Recent studies have shown that as naturally as women gain a few pounds premenstrually, they lose them immediately afterwards. In one study, the control group struggled to control food cravings. They didn't gain weight, but they didn't lose weight once menstruation was over, either! You *need* more calories at this time. Many women report cravings for milk products and green vegetables, which balance out the typical chocolate/sugar cravings that provide only a temporary lift.

5.  **Exercise** An all-over, aerobic routine is especially good. Aerobics stimulate circulation and elimination, thus counteracting symptoms like bloating, cramping, and fatigue.

6.  **Stay warm** To compensate for circulatory disruptions, stay cosy. Wear socks, wrap up in a blanket, take a sauna, turn up the heat, and wear loose, comfortable clothing (forget the tight jeans).

7.  **Make space for yourself** Take time off, find ways to defer responsibilities, or duck out of them altogether if they really are excessive. Make time to be alone, to do things that make you feel good; in a word, indulge.

8.  **Have sex if you want to** A little sex goes a long way towards alleviating premenstrual tension. Be yourself – weepy, passionate, outrageous, outspoken – make sex work for *you*. Masturbate, enjoy your body.

9.  **Celebrate when your period begins** Do some sort of letting-go-of-the-old ritual, burn letters, discard objects that symbolise entanglement, make affirmations of ending and new beginning.

wonderful book, *Red Flower*, Dena Taylor documents a
wide range of response to menstrual symptoms, featuring
cross-cultural perspectives. Particularly noteworthy is the
desire for seclusion; women speak of wanting to curl up in
bed and relax, sleep by themselves and avoid going out in
public. Some speak of wanting to be only with women, and
how nice it would be to have a special place (like a hut)
where they could gather with others who were also
menstruating. I tend to think of this time as visionary for
women, both personally and collectively.

Ernest Hartmann, author of *The Biology of Dreaming*,
notes that women dream most between days 25 and 30 of
the cycle. These dreams are often sexual, sometimes violent
and aggressive, as compared to dreams during ovulation
which are generally more soothing and somewhat passive.
Specifically, dream images during menstruation include
speaking animals, animals with men's heads, violent acts
and broken eggshells, whereas ovulating women report
dreaming of babies, fragile things, jewels, eggs and their
mothers.[4] Women tend to dream about having sex with
their partners or dear friends when ovulating; when menstruating, sex with strangers.

In fact, it is the premenstrual phase which is most noted
for dreams of violence and death. This makes sense, really,
as it is the lowest point hormonally and the turning point
as well. I've found myself melancholy and wondering what
I would do if one of my children died, or sometimes have
feelings of inadequacy or despair over difficult situations in
my life that I fear will never change. When I start flowing,
my emotions loosen up and I become myself again. It is
particularly interesting that PMS is apparently more severe
when sleep is inadequate; Hartmann conjectures that
perhaps women need more sleep at this time for the natural
release of dreaming. (Note, however, that tranquillisers

## MOON PHASE ENERGIES AND MENSTRUATION

**Waxing moon menstruation**

The waxing moon is a time of growth, of new processes coming into play and of new beginnings. This is a time to turn inwards and pay attention to one's own wisdom, as well as a time to learn new things and make discoveries.

In Native American culture, the animal of the waxing moon is the raven, who stands for exchange of knowledge and the flight of the soul. In ancient Greek culture the goddess Persephone, who walked the underworld, is the guardian of this phase.

**Full moon menstruation**

The full moon is outwardly focused: a time to bring to bear, to work and to do. Whereas the waxing moon correlates to daybreak, the full moon is like high noon, a time when things may be revealed. This is a charged phase and a challenging one emotionally, when the dragon nature of menstruating women is fully evident.

The animal of the full moon, in Native American culture, is the phoenix, who burns to ashes and then rises anew, and the goddess is Ishtar, Red Goddess of Babylon.

**Waning moon menstruation**

The waning moon parallels sunset, a time when energy subsides and stabilises. Now is the time to firm up plans, substantiate discoveries, verify knowledge and let ideas bear fruit.

In Native American culture, the animal of this phase is the she-bear, who signifies the womb and is therefore productive. And in ancient Greek culture, it is the goddess Demeter, who signifies the harvest.

**New moon menstruation**

The new moon is inwardly focused and the time for contemplation, reflection, germination. This is the midnight phase, also a time for rest and recuperation. Subconscious memories and anxieties rise to the surface, events are reviewed.

The animal of this phase is the toad: wise, slippery, solitary and untouchable (due to her poisonous exterior). The goddess is Hecate, the crone, the reaper, the dark one.

Adapted from *Dragontime* by Luisa Francia (New York, Ash Tree Publishing, 1988) and sleeping pills sometimes prescribed for PMS may repress or inhibit dreaming.)

In the Native American tradition, some tribes believe that a girl's dreams at menarche (her first period) tell of her mission or direction in life. According to Brooke Medicine Eagle, Native American woman and shaman, the most prophetic dreams and visions of the future, including unimaginable events like the coming of the white man, were 'brought to the people through the Moon Lodge', or women's ritual place of seclusion during menstruation.[5]

If you are curious about your dreams at this point in your cycle but generally don't remember them, begin by keeping paper and pen by the bed. And be sure to record your recollections immediately upon awaking, even if it's four o'clock in the morning. Despite what you may think, you won't remember them later.

Not surprisingly, women often report yet another peak of sexual activity several days into the menstrual flow. For some, the first two or three days are unappealing due to general messiness, but as the flow shifts from heavy to moderate, passion picks up. Says Nancy, 'Frankly, I like sex best when I'm having my period. I don't have to worry about pregnancy (I know my cycle) and I'm in a certain mood – feisty, steamy. I'm pre-lubricated too, and you know, I don't mind the blood all over everything: it's erotic to me and my partner.' Or, as Jane says, 'I feel free, I feel primal, I feel connected to my power. The blood turns me on: it's a symbol of life, the colour of passion.' And from Ana, 'Actually, I think it's hormones, coming back around, picking up again. I know it's not the usual image, but I feel fresh, renewed. I don't think about the past. I think about the future.'

Some experts in women's sexuality suggest that taboos on intercourse during menstruation may have been due to women's unusually high sex drive and increased orgasmic capacity, causing inordinate male attention and resulting social disruption.[6] On the other hand, in the Tantric tradition, the most powerful sexual rites require that women be menstruating for the 'blending of female red and male white'.[7]

A major area of confusion for many women regards whether or not conception is possible when menstruating. This was, in fact, one of the questions most often missed by the public on the recent (1990) Kinsey nationwide sex quiz. The correct answer is yes, although only rarely does this occur. In truth, the body does not menstruate and ovulate simultaneously, but the two can occur back to back. For example, a woman with a 21 day cycle might ovulate as early as day six or seven (remember that the post-ovulatory phase is fixed at 14 days). If she also has a five day menstrual flow, there might already be mucus present on day five that could keep sperm viable until the egg is released a day or two later. Conception on days one, two and three is virtually unheard of, particularly when the flow is heavy. Yet the fear of pregnancy may prevent women from enjoying the free days that do exist at this point and making the most of them.

And where does this bring us? Back to the beginning – we've come full circle on our hormonal journey. However, there are definite variations for women suffering from gynaecological problems and illnesses, or for those under the influence of certain contraceptive methods.

## HEALTH PROBLEMS THAT AFFECT THE CYCLE

Failure to menstruate altogether is called amenorrhoea, and may be caused by insufficient body fat, tumours of the hypothalamus or pituitary gland, thyroid disease, diseases affecting the central nervous system, diabetes or other chronic diseases, destruction of the endometrium (uterine lining) by excessive curettage (as used in D and C procedures or abortions), drug or alcohol addiction, adrenal disorders, ovarian cysts, or certain drugs. More often, a missed period is caused by stress, or possibly by rigorous athletic training,

There are several diseases and conditions that so affect the cycle as to require in-depth examination. Endometriosis has become almost commonplace in recent years, and is a major cause of infertility. Here is what happens: endometrial tissue somehow escapes from inside the uterus to implant itself on the outside of the pelvic organs, and proceeds to function as usual by going through cyclic changes. However, as there is no natural way for this tissue to be shed (as normally happens in menstruation), it will scar over repeatedly until adhesions (abnormal attachments between the pelvic structures) form. This may cause the uterus or tubes to twist, may prevent eggs from being released, or may lead to the development of ovarian cysts which ultimately disrupt ovulation.

What causes endometriosis? One theory is that a scarred or tightly closed cervix (due possibly to pelvic infection or traumatic abortion) may not allow a full release of the menses, which then pass out of the ends of the Fallopian tubes and become imbedded on adjacent pelvic tissues. Symptoms include abnormal bleeding and pain with ovulation, with menstruation, with intercourse or bowel movements. As mentioned earlier, infertility may be another symptom. However, pregnancy can cure the problem, since the natural hormonal changes of that process tend to shrink the implants almost completely. Sometimes birth control pills or other medications prove helpful, although alternative approaches such as acupuncture, homeopathy or herbal treatments may work as well or better.

Cutler has speculated that sex during menstruation may cause endometriosis. However, since her study population was extremely limited and no account was made of previous cervical/uterine trauma, her results are inconclusive at best.[9]

Yet another ailment known as polycystic ovarian disease (or Stein-Leventhal syndrome) causes serious hormonal imbalance: low FSH, high oestrogen, erratic surges of LH, low progesterone and elevated male hormones. The cycle attacked by polycystic disease sees no rhythmic rise and fall of these substances, but levels that remain constant and unchanging. A follicle swells but fails to release an egg, then fills with fluid and becomes a cyst. Although the cells around the egg produce male hormones that the body converts to oestrogen, this merely fools the body into thinking an egg is ready to be released. The pituitary gland responds by cutting back FSH and releasing LH, which normally would cause the egg to break away. But this does not happen; instead the follicle/cyst continues to enlarge. At worst, the cyst might rupture and cause internal bleeding. At the same time, high oestrogen levels prevent the uterus from shedding so there are no menses, and this build-up of the endometrium increases the risk of uterine cancer.

How might a woman know she has polycystic disease? Often, the cyst will cause pain or discomfort in the pelvic region. She would notice significant changes in menstruation, and might also observe abnormal growth of facial and/or body hair in response to elevated male hormones.

Yet another condition that drastically alters a woman's cycle is hysterectomy. Of course, if all the reproductive organs are removed, immediate menopause ensues. Sometimes, even if the uterus is diseased, the ovaries are fine and can be left in place so that normal hormonal production continues. For further information on complete hysterectomy see Chapter Six.

Beyond these conditions, there are factors apt to affect the cycle of any woman living in typical contemporary fashion. Artificial lighting may disrupt the influences of moonlight and cause irregularities in the cycle, particularly if one lives in an area with a street lamp right outside the bedroom window. Blackout blinds can be used to reproduce more natural conditions of living out of doors; the blinds should be down completely around new moon time.

And then there is the busy pace of life, which is particularly gruelling for a woman having to coordinate numerous activities. We all have daily, personal biorhythms: times throughout the day when we naturally seek out food, rest, or stimulation. Some women are morning types, some more nocturnal. Frequently, our personal rhythms are at odds with social routine; we may not, for example, feel like eating at traditional meal times.

Learning to follow one's daily rhythms is important. For many of us, as busy and out in the world as we are, there is nothing more soothing and healing than time alone, a day off once in awhile to do exactly as we please. Living life in whatever way comes easiest to us means following our instincts for eating, resting, exercising and lovemaking, along with our impulses to socialise, create, or be solitary.

Fast-food, stimulants like coffee, sugar and chocolate, or sedatives like alcohol, all obscure our natural biorhythms. This doesn't mean we must give these up, but we do need to keep an eye on our intake. These substances tend to debilitate our bodies and place stress on our systems so that we lose vitamins and minerals and need to take supplements. Moreover, when we are less than healthy our emotional reactions are extreme, our responses to various

## HERBS FOR MENSTRUATION

- **Basil** (*Ocimum bascilicum*), particularly the fresh leaf, stimulates bleeding, invigorates and lifts feelings of depression. A favourite way to take basil is by making pesto dishes; serving it with pasta is especially good as the carbohydrates are stabilising at the onset of menstruation.

- **Catmint** (*Nepeta cataria*) is pain killing, cramp easing, soothing and calming. It is further renowned for its ability to ease colic in newborn infants.

- **Ginger** (*Zingiber officinale*) stimulates circulation, warms and balances the body, and helps dispel gastro-intestinal upsets.

- **Life root** (*Senecio aureus*) can be taken by tincture: five to ten drops daily help regulate the cycle and ease PMS. It can also help relieve severe cramps, both uterine and intestinal. Herbal lore has it that life root blossoms were found carefully placed on the oldest grave known.[8] It is especially effective taken long-term.

- **Motherwort** (*Leonurus cardiaca*) is most effective by tincture: take ten drops to relax, fifteen drops to ease menstrual pain. Motherwort is also used for hot flushes during menopause, and to ease labour pains.

- **Nettle** (*Urtica dioica*) helps get rid of excess water and reduce bloating, while strengthening the kidneys and adrenals. It also provides key minerals, such as calcium and iron, vitamin K and carotene, and plenty of protein. It is especially useful when there is excessive bleeding.

- **Raspberry** (*Rubus species*) is said to represent women's passion and life force. Raspberry tea eases PMS and tones the uterus; it is mood-elevating and brings, according to Luisa Francia, 'passionate menstruation'. It is the beverage of choice for women throughout pregnancy and postpartum.

- **Rosemary** (*Rosmarinus officinalis*), either oil or leaf, is strengthening and stabilising to the body. It stimulates bleeding, and helps keep energy high and consistent during menstruation.

With all herbs, source and processing make all the difference. Familiarise yourself with fresh herbs available in your area, and seek out distributors who carry organic products. Good tinctures are dated for reference, and generally appear clear, not muddy.

phases in the cycle become more exaggerated, and our abilities to rise to challenges day-by-day become impaired.

That our modern diet is also devoid of tonic and medicinal herbs is unfortunate, but this is something we can work to change. Herbs are allies to health and harmony; when one starts using herbs for self-improvement, desires for harmful substances or less-than-healthy foods often begin to fall away.

## THE EFFECTS OF CONTRACEPTIVE METHODS

We'll start with oral contraceptives. Put bluntly, the birth control pill completely wipes out the cyclical pattern of emotional and sexual response we've discussed. The Pill works by effecting a state of mini-pregnancy, with hormone levels high enough to trick the body into believing it's pregnant so that ovulation does not occur. Most formulas combine oestrogen and progesterone; others use progesterone only (the mini-pill). Each of these hormones, should the dose prove excessive, is responsible for specific side effects like weight gain, acne, breast tenderness, nausea, headaches (other than migraines), fatigue, etc. (See the box on page 43.) A woman's response to a particular formula is somewhat unpredictable because much depends on her pre-existing balance and sensitivities. This is why a gynaecologist may suggest five or six brands before discovering one that is satisfactory.

Ultimately, though, the day-to-day hormone mix is uniform. A woman on birth control pills is hormonally monotone, always the same. Gone are the natural peaks of oestrogen and progesterone. Gone are the creativity and passion during ovulation, the intense desire immediately before or during menstruation. Gone too is the psychological richness associated with the above, plus the benefits

## OESTROGEN AND PROGESTERONE IMBALANCES

*Signs of Oestrogen Excess:*
- nausea and vomiting
- dizziness
- oedema
- leg cramps
- increase in breast size
- chloasma (brown pigmentation on face)
- visual changes
- hypertension
- certain headaches (vascular)

*Signs of Oestrogen Deficiency:*
- early spotting (days one to 14)
- reduced menstrual flow
- nervousness
- painful intercourse due to vaginal changes

*Signs of Progesterone Excess:*
- increased appetite
- tiredness
- depression, mood changes
- breast tenderness
- vaginal yeast infection
- oily skin and scalp
- hirsutism (excess body hair)

*Signs of Progesterone Deficiency:*
- late spotting and break-through bleeding (days 15 to 21)
- heavy menstrual flow, with clots
- decreased breast size

of cyclic completion and renewal. For there is no real menstruation when on the Pill; it takes ovulation to trigger the full build-up and release of the uterine lining. All Pill users have is a little break-through bleeding when they've taken the last of the batch and hormone levels drop temporarily. This flow is lighter and typically uniform, without variation in length and/or consistency.

Even sequential pills (triphasic), which attempt to duplicate a more natural rhythm of oestrogen and progesterone, produce an artificial pattern ultimately foreign to a woman's own. When clients tell me of their desire to get off the Pill, albeit with some reluctance, they often cite the primary reason as wanting to be more in touch with their bodies. As we talk further, what they really seem to miss is being in touch with themselves, their own unique mind–body blend. It's disturbing to think that artificial hormonal influences could alter personality, but considering the singular powers of oestrogen and progesterone, such is clearly the case.

Another complaint from women on the Pill is, ironically enough, decreased interest in sex. This is probably due to general disruption of pituitary function, which affects the release of androgens from the adrenals. Then again, freedom from fear of pregnancy may be aphrodisiac, though not the same as biologically-induced desire.

As mentioned earlier, the Pill may be therapeutic for certain gynaecological problems, such as endometriosis or pathologically painful menstruation. Nevertheless, it's important to remember that relief obtained in these cases merely masks underlying causes. Again, acupuncture may effectively re-educate the system to a more harmonious condition.

Acupuncture may also be useful for women coming off the Pill. It is not uncommon for women to miss a period or two; the body has forgotten what to do, so to speak, and needs to get back on track. If the rhythm is lost for six months or more, a combination of acupuncture and herbs can stimulate pituitary secretion of LH and FSH, with appropriate ovarian response. I find this preferable to the use of Clomid, a potent fertility drug notorious for causing multiple pregnancies. Problems with delayed cyclical function are much more common after the age of 30; ironically, a time when women often quit the Pill specifically to get pregnant.

Now, let's consider the effects of the IUD on a woman's cycle. With the exception of the Progestasert, the IUD does not directly affect hormonal balance. However, many women do report heavier periods with greater discomfort. Originally, women receiving the IUD were told that these problems were merely mechanical, that the device caused low-grade irritation with side effects of cramping and increased flow. What they were not told was that the IUD does not actually prevent conception, merely implantation of the already fertilised ovum. After all, there is no mechanical barrier to prevent the sperm from meeting the egg. The so-called heavy periods with the IUD are in fact spontaneous miscarriages, month after month after month.

Thus the hormonal effects of the IUD, though indirect, are quite drastic; with conception, dramatic changes in the levels of oestrogen and progesterone occur. I recall piecing this realisation together many years ago while wearing an IUD. I couldn't wait to get it out! Just the idea of miscarrying over and over, plus going through intense hormonal changes on a nearly continuous basis, was physically and emotionally offensive to me. I realise that certain women are satisfied with the IUD and consider it a godsend. But so extensively has it been linked to fertility problems (due to uterine scarring, tubal pregnancy and rupture) that it is nearly off the market, except for the Progestasert. This works something like the mini-pill: increased levels of progesterone on a daily basis do not prevent the egg from maturing, but do chemically alter the cervical mucus in a way that makes it inhospitable to sperm. Again, hormonal aberration from a woman's norm

**HERBAL SOURCES OF OESTROGEN
AND PROGESTERONE**

*Oestrogen Producing Herbs:*
- blue cohosh
- black cohosh
- basil
- sage
- blackcurrant
- liquorice
- raspberry leaf

*Progesterone Inducing Herbs:*
- sarsaparilla
- wild yam root
- tansy
- chaste tree (vitex)

may lead to excess bleeding and persistent imbalance that is difficult to correct. The nearly foolproof method of tubal ligation, long touted as having virtually no side effects, merits closer investigation. Numerous studies published in the 1980s show that certain procedures, such as high-frequency and endocoagulation methods, cause hormonal and menstrual cycle disruption in nearly one-third of all cases. Diminished oestrogen and progesterone levels may even contribute to early menopause, or the onset of menopausal symptoms. Other methods, like the Hulka clip, seem to produce good results and maintain hormonal balance.[10]

What about the barrier methods? Obviously, these have no physiological effect on a woman's cycle. Local effects and inconveniences are considerable, including chemical irritation from spermicide, lack of spontaneity, messiness and reduced sensation.

My extensive experience with the cervical cap has led me to favour it both personally and professionally. As compared to the diaphragm, it uses very little spermicide: no additional applications are required for repeated intercourse. It can be left in place for several days, and is small enough to be virtually undetectable. A little-known fact about the diaphragm is that although it feels snug when first placed, the vagina expands so much with arousal that even an oversized fit will move and slide around freely during intercourse, readily admitting seminal fluid. Thus the jelly inside the diaphragm becomes so diluted that more must be added before having sex again, hopefully to catch the sperm before they get over the rim. But the cap fits the cervix securely with suction, forming a stable mechanical barrier. In addition, when the user is fertile, the cap retains her mucous secretion so that the natural, sperm-killing acidity of the vagina is maintained (seminal fluid is alkaline, as is fertile mucus; sperm need this in fresh, abundant supply or they die rapidly). Thus the cap works with a woman's chemistry rather than against it, and is more truly a barrier method than the diaphragm, which relies heavily on chemical effect.

A bonus of cap use is increased familiarity with one's cycle; it is fairly easy to see what phase you are in depending on the type of secretion your cap collects. Also, women who use the cap report less yeast and other vaginal infections than with the diaphragm, since chemical disturbance of vaginal flora is virtually non-existent.

Having used a diaphragm for 14 years, as well as having fitted them extensively, I know the frustrations of overriding discomfort and disrupted spontaneity. There were numerous occasions I was tempted to leave the diaphragm in the drawer, or toss it into the dustbin. Eventually, I recognised that much of my resistance was due to reduced levels of sensation during intercourse. Around this time, news of the Graffenburg spot (or G-spot) hit the press, and suddenly it all made sense. By virtue of its design, the front rim of the diaphragm must displace the G-spot in order to lodge behind the pubic bone. No wonder I couldn't feel as much! Once I learned fertility awareness and could safely use my diaphragm only when necessary, I was able to make a real comparison. The problem was solved completely when I switched to the cap; it sits way back on the cervix alone, nowhere near the G-spot!

As mentioned earlier, some women use fertility awareness as birth control, abstaining during the ovulatory phase. However, this may cause considerable frustration as intense desire must routinely be ignored or expressed in ways other than vaginal/penile intercourse. Increasingly, women in my practice choose to combine fertility awareness with a barrier method of some kind.

A number of women alternate use of the cap or diaphragm with condoms. They say it feels good to share the responsibility, switching back and forth from month to month, or from time to time. A comment from Suzanne: 'My partner and I had run the gamut in birth control, and ended up with barrier methods for safety's sake. But it didn't feel right to me to always be the one who had to remember to take charge. It's nice when my partner uses a condom: I can just sit back and relax, and I like the feeling of my body being completely natural. It helps me enjoy sex more.'

In the next chapter, we will look at sex and the child bearing cycle, including the fertility dance leading up to conception. Particularly if a woman is aware of her rhythms, she and her partner will be likely to experience conception as it occurs. We will also consider how out-of-sync desires for conception can affect the tone, ease and frequency of sexual sharing in a relationship.

1. 'Women Score High During Ovulation', *San Francisco Chronicle* (1985)
2. Cutler, Winnifred B., *Love Cycles* (New York, Villard Books, 1991)
3. Taylor, Dena, *Red Flower: Rethinking Menstruation* (Freedom, California, Crossing Press, 1988)
4. Shuttle, Penelope and Redgrove, Peter, *The Wise Wound* (New York, Richard Marek, 1978)
5. Taylor, *Red Flower*
6. Sherfey, Mary Jane, *The Nature and Evolution of Female Sexuality* (New York, Random House, 1973)
7. Walker, Barbara G., *The Woman's Encyclopedia of Myths and Secrets* (San Francisco, Harper & Row, 1983)
8. Francia, Luisa, *Dragontime*, (Woodstock, New York, Ash Tree Publishing, 1988)
9. Cutler, *Love Cycles*
10. Jovanovic, Lois and Subak-Sharpe, Genell, *Hormones, the Woman's Answer Book*, (New York, Ballantine, 1987)

# 3

# Sexuality, pregnancy and birth

Being aware of your monthly cycles means you will also be more apt to notice your biologically programmed desire for conception from time to time. The urge may emerge only in mid-cycle dreams, or you may find yourself fantasising about babies and birth with increasing frequency. Sometimes, when the desire for a baby has built up over a period of time, women report startling feelings during lovemaking that conception is somehow imminent, as though birth control can barely hold back the forces of creation – the dam about to burst. Some women even report visions of waiting spirits, little boys or girls. As one said, 'We were in the midst of lovemaking that was overwhelming from the moment it began, so very powerful, when suddenly I got the image of a little, blond, curly haired boy and I *knew* that I could conceive that child, that it wanted to come to me. I tried to tell my partner about it later, but he wasn't ready to hear it – he thought I was fabricating, I guess. But I never will forget the intensity, the clarity, the ultra-real quality of that moment. From then on, I knew it was just a matter of time and that we were destined to have a child together.'

No one can really say exactly what brings on such revelations, but they clearly go beyond mere biology. I think couples deeply in love build up so much intensity in their relationship that it eventually overflows and demands an outlet, an extension. Women speak of this fecund state in somewhat mystical terms. Joanne recalls, 'I felt like the veil between worlds, this and another place of souls, began to fall away. Soon, all we had to do was touch, and the awareness of that other place, new life just waiting, was all around us.'

It follows that couples who have this awareness are likely to be conscious of conception if and when it does occur. Looking back, I can recall the exact moment when each of my children was conceived. Even now, I am surprised by how vivid the memories are, every detail of the environment and the mood is crystal clear because my sensory awareness was at its peak. Each time, just moments after orgasm, there was a period of truth and realisation, extraordinary and profound, that left me sure and shaking with the knowledge that I had conceived. There was no turning back. I was forever changed!

This picture is somewhat at odds with contemporary notions of conscious conception, which paint it out to be thoroughly planned, predicted and controlled. More often, at least according to my midwifery clientele, it's less a matter of control than surrender, with conception happening to the couple, rather than the other way around. Commonly, they report, 'Well, it wasn't exactly planned, it happened a bit sooner than we expected, but we were open to it and we pretty much knew right away.'

For others, things are not so easy and spontaneous. Couples who have struggled with infertility, and have reduced their lovemaking to a by-the-clock method so that chances of conception are maximised, may feel so much anxiety, sadness and frustration that immediate awareness of conception is blocked. These same emotions are felt by women who have miscarried and are trying again. Women who have had traumatic abortions may also struggle psychologically, particularly if they have not made their peace with previous losses.

And sometimes, a woman stands alone in her desire to conceive. She and her partner can't come to terms with the issue, or perhaps he is adamantly against becoming a father. There is no easy solution or quick-fix here.

As a culture, we've not yet dealt with the unnaturalness of ongoing contraception in intimate relationships. Here is an area where women must take the lead and speak of the emotional turmoil and hardship contraceptive compliance can cause. This is not to say that contraception hasn't been a boon for women, enabling them to assume social and political roles of great significance by being free to choose whether and when to have children. But I've heard far too many clients in their late thirties or forties speak wistfully of having children someday when their lives are 'together', only to become severely traumatised when they finally realise that it's too late.

Partly, this approach to parenthood is endemic to a society that provides virtually no financial or social support for child-bearing women or young families. But also it reveals our cultural penchant for perfection, our overriding emphasis on material conformity and the acquisition of goods as prerequisite to happiness. At odds with this are the natural, biological phases in the life cycle. Nature did not design us to have children when we have material and emotional mastery, or we would be having them in our fifties and sixties. Through parenting we grow and develop, we learn to give unconditionally, to accept small strides day-by-day and to make the most of the way things are, rather than wishing them to be different. These are important lessons in human maturation that are otherwise difficult to come by. Nevertheless, when today's woman finds herself desirous of children, she is bombarded with rational considerations and beset with doubts so that the pro-creation impulse, at once biological, creative, spiritual and evolutionary, tends to be crushed. This, we must work to change. We must reclaim the inherent power of our ability to conceive!

When pregnancy does occur, women undergo a complex series of hormonal, physical and psychological changes that profoundly affect identity and self-expression. To some women, especially at first, the pregnant state seems utter chaos. Actually, though, pregnancy can be divided into definite stages and phases that do make sense when viewed as a whole. Most simply, pregnancy is comprised of three trimesters, each lasting approximately 13 weeks and each with its own challenges and characteristics.

### THE FIRST TRIMESTER

Even though women seldom show their pregnancies at this stage, major hormonal and physiological changes are taking place. When conception occurs, progesterone and oestrogen levels do not dip down as in a typical monthly cycle, but rise even higher, to several times their normal levels. This causes changes throughout the body. The thyroid gland enlarges, which raises the body's metabolic rate to provide the necessary energy for foetal development and other demands of pregnancy on the mother's body. The adrenal glands produce additional aldosterone to help counter the sodium loss that might otherwise occur with such high levels of oestrogen and progesterone. This may account for the fact that many women feel a decreased desire for sex at the beginning of pregnancy, at least in the first weeks.

But this is not the only reason sexual desire may be curtailed. Morning sickness, which occurs with the body's adjustment to elevated hormone levels, is hardly conducive to cuddling and carrying on. In fact, many women feel exceedingly vulnerable in this condition and desire or request new sorts of nurturing behaviours from their partners. The simple act of being brought a bit of dry toast first thing in the morning means more to a woman than comfort alone; it's a measure of her partner's ongoing commitment and concern, and as such, can lead to increased trust and intimacy once nausea is overcome. Other physical changes involve the breasts and particularly the nipples, which become hypersensitive to touch. Alicia reports: 'My breasts are rather small and I'm not that confident about them, but when I'm pregnant, they become a focus in our lovemaking.' Cheryl sums it up succinctly: 'My partner and I have never gotten more pleasure from my breasts than when I was pregnant.'

Another inconvenience of early pregnancy is frequent urination, due to uterine enlargement and pressure on the bladder. However, increased circulation in pelvic tissues as a mechanism for uterine growth can also lead to pelvic engorgement, similar to that in premenstrual or ovulatory phases of the monthly cycle. This may cause a woman to wonder what's hit her, and whether her desire for deep and forceful penetration is really safe. There has been much debate on this subject over the years; theories regarding deleterious effects of intercourse and orgasm on mother and baby have come and gone. For a while it was thought that orgasm should be strictly avoided, lest subsequent uterine contractions cause oxygen deprivation for the baby. There is no doubt that orgasm causes uterine activity, but to a degree so minor as to have no serious impact on placental circulation. Additionally, increased heart rate and deeper breathing on the part of the mother tend naturally to compensate for any adverse effects.

There have also been moralistic admonitions against 'exposing the foetus to an atmosphere of carnal desire'. Let's hope that one is behind us. More recently, there were studies linking uterine and/or foetal infection with intercourse in the last trimester. However, these findings proved inconclusive due to variables such as stress levels, dietary habits and pre-existing health conditions.

On the other hand, if there is a history of miscarriage or episodes of bleeding in the current pregnancy, sexual activity may well be curtailed, at least until the first trimester is over. It is noteworthy that one in four women have some bleeding in early pregnancy, yet only one in ten miscarry. Particularly if the bleeding coincides with the time of the month menstruation would ordinarily occur, there is less cause for concern. In this case, it seems that the body maintains its old rhythm for a while until new hormonal levels are established, nothing more.

If there is a history of premature labour or birth, sexual activity may be forbidden later in pregnancy, depending on whether the cervix shows any signs of premature softening or opening. Sometimes a woman must stay in bed for some time until her baby is ready to be born, with intercourse and orgasm strictly taboo.

Barring these exceptions, sex brings the benefits of increased pelvic circulation, release of tension and overall muscle toning that naturally occur with intercourse and are particularly helpful as preparation for birth. There are immense psychological benefits as well, particularly in the face of rapid growth and change. Many couples describe their sexual encounters in pregnancy as rebonding experiences, akin in tone to those in the initial phase of their relationship. No wonder, for both are assuming new roles and becoming new people, and are getting to know certain aspects of one another for the first time. And for many there is tremendous freedom in not having to worry about birth control.

A woman's desire in the first trimester may also have something to do with the sex of the child she is carrying. At about six to eight weeks, when the brain is developing, male foetuses are exposed to an enormous dose of testosterone, the level of which is four times that throughout infancy and childhood.[1] Surely, this will have some impact on the mother, quite possibly increasing her libido. By the same token, it may be that a mother's ability to recognise the sex of her unborn has some hormonal basis, since surges of male hormone continue to occur in boys at regular intervals during gestation.

Precisely how the demands of early pregnancy will influence a woman's sexuality depends on her personality, her self-esteem, her desire for the baby, the stability of her primary relationship(s), and various other psycho-social factors. Generally, women in our culture feel somewhat frightened upon confirmation of pregnancy; excited perhaps, but apprehensive nonetheless. This is really a very normal reaction, considering that most of us know little or nothing about child bearing, have never witnessed a birth or even held and comforted a baby. Along with the thrill of being pregnant may come well-founded anxiety about joining the ranks of one of the least acknowledged and most underprivileged groups in our society – mothers! The newly pregnant woman soon learns that society considers motherhood a personal venture that must somehow be done 'on the side', squeezed onto an already loaded palette of responsibilities. It is never too early to begin the work of establishing a support system, whether by getting together with other expectant mothers or by forging new alliances with female relatives.

In my book, *Energetic Pregnancy*, I explore in some detail women's reactions to specific stages of child bearing according to personality type. A physically fit woman, for example, may find the natural softening of her body and loss of emotional control due to hormone swings at the onset of pregnancy to be fairly excruciating. She is apt to complain that her body doesn't work anymore; no longer can she make her way by physical force alone. Naturally, this will affect her sexual self-image. The key to her adjustment is to let her feelings flow, while learning more about the unique capabilities of her 'new' body.

More emotional women may be quite the opposite, glorying in the heightened sensitivities of pregnancy and enjoying sex as much as ever. However, increased needs for food and exercise may go unnoticed, leading to reduced energy and emotional instability. An emotional woman needs to set feelings aside once in a while in order to focus on her body. She also needs to learn specifically about nutrition and the physiology of pregnancy: concrete, factual information that will offset her tendency to be fanatic.

Then again, the mentally-led woman, with a penchant for control and having everything in place, may make her adaptation by the book and yet feel disoriented by surges of emotion and extreme mental states quite beyond her experience. She must find a way to release emotion, connecting mind and body through movement, massage, or anything that facilitates spontaneity and trust in her inner voice. This can add an entirely new dimension to her sexuality. Like the other types, she will face fresh challenges as pregnancy progresses; accordingly, her sexual attitudes and behaviours will continue to come up for scrutiny and transformation.

An oft underrated aspect of pregnancy is the sweeping impact of elevated hormones on a woman's psyche. Or perhaps we hear only the downside, the negative view that paints expectant mothers as borderline crazies, forgetful, hopelessly moody and foolishly preoccupied. It is, after all, our cultural tendency to consider pregnant women child-like, dressing them in puffed sleeves with little-girl prints. Beyond such minimising and insulting definitions of their psychological state, we must listen to what pregnant women tell us about themselves. 'I've never felt better in my life,' is a typical response or, 'I'm finally fulfilled, really myself at last.' Consider how well non-pregnant women feel at the monthly oestrogen peak – confident, powerful, creative, physically alert and strong – and juxtapose this with pregnancy when levels are even higher. Elevated progesterone also contributes to a heightened state of awareness, adding an extra-sensory dimension.

### THE SECOND TRIMESTER

The mid-point of pregnancy is the point of stability. Women love this phase; they feel great and look radiant with pregnant glow. Around 20 weeks, a mother usually feels her baby move for the first time, an event known as quickening. An interesting term, connoting awakening and accelerated awareness. Who quickens, though: baby, mother or both? In any case, there is no doubt that women at this stage in pregnancy have extraordinary powers of perception, concentration and recuperation, all of which enhance sexual expression. General equilibrium further contributes to increased libido, as all the basic hormonal and mechanical adjustments of pregnancy have taken place and now begin to blend with the mother's own efforts to eat, exercise and rest responsively. Beyond simple awareness of foetal movement, some women say they start to get a sense of the baby's personality by how it moves, its rhythms of activity and rest. It follows that a woman might also begin to incorporate her feelings for the baby in lovemaking, as the duo becomes a triad.

Alice, mother of three, puts it this way:

> With each of my pregnancies, I became familiar with my baby a little sooner. The first time, I could barely believe I had a baby in me at all, it was just so overwhelming. Then, I remember an incident with my second. I had the flu and was quite sick, and after a rather violent episode of vomiting I said out loud, 'Oh, I hope she's all right,' and yes, I had a girl! With the last, though, I felt I knew him right from the start. I would tell people that he was very active, but sweet, and they'd look at me indulgently. It's easy to see now that I was right.

And what about sex with this awareness?

> When it comes to sex, I also felt that I had more ability each time to communicate my knowledge of the baby to my partner. Our deep connection to one another during lovemaking began to include the baby, too, especially with the last. This was so wonderful – memories I will always treasure. I was with child and with the man I love, both at the same time. I felt completely fulfilled.

Lesbian mothers report that their natural tendency to align with their partner hormonally – oestrogen peaks and menses in synchrony – makes possible an even deeper physical empathy in pregnancy that enables both parents to know the baby intimately, even though the non-pregnant partner has no biological link. From Jen, 'Sex with Anne when she was pregnant was an ever so much enhanced version of what we had known before. I felt very connected to the baby. Knowing Anne so well, it was easy to differentiate the baby's energy from hers.'

Besides oestrogen and progesterone, there is yet another hormone that enters in at this stage: oxytocin, otherwise known as the love hormone. It is secreted by the pituitary's posterior lobe in response to sexual arousal, breast stimulation and orgasm, and is naturally present in higher and higher amounts as pregnancy progresses. Oxytocin is a fascinating hormone, found not only to enhance fertility in women by increasing movement of the Fallopian tubes, but to increase sperm count in men when given by nasal spray. It has also been shown to alleviate symptoms of depression in laboratory animals, thus it is sometimes called the happy hormone.[2] Consider the feeling of well-being after orgasm, the ecstasy of afterglow, and it is easy to see why.

Putting all these factors together – increased libido, elevated oestrogen, progesterone and oxytocin levels plus increased vaginal engorgement and sensitivity – it's no wonder many women feel virtually insatiable, surprising both themselves and their partners. Jeanine states:

To be perfectly honest, I masturbated almost every day. It felt very natural to me. Jack was worried that sex would hurt the baby, but our doctor told him to forget his fears. My vagina was so pliable – he could put two or three fingers inside me and I still wanted more, more pressure. I felt like I was opening up for the baby, but when I had orgasms my muscles squeezed so tight Jack said it practically hurt.

Let's take a closer look at men's reactions to sex in pregnancy. If a man feels concern about jeopardising the pregnancy during the first trimester, his fear may be further compounded by feeling the baby move in the second. The average male believes a woman's system to be somewhat delicate, and the idea of deep thrusting in the general area that a baby is developing makes certain men squeamish. But there is more. Many men struggle with conflicting images of madonna/lover, unable to blend the two and hence uncertain of how to relate to their partner sexually. That a woman nurturing new life might also be blatantly lustful and erotic is the merger of two culturally disparate aspects of femininity into one very powerful whole. (Witness the stir caused by Demi Moore's infamous pose in *Vanity Fair*: eight months pregnant and wearing nothing more than black bra, panties and spike heels!) For the outright misogynist, the man deeply at odds with his feminine side, or even the ordinary guy who up to this point has had no idea that such a configuration was possible, there is a strong likelihood of sexual inhibition or shutdown.

What's a woman to do if this occurs? Her midwife or doctor should be able to reassure the expectant father, refer him to a support group or to individual counselling. Nevertheless, deeply ingrained beliefs of this kind are not easy to change, thus the situation may not readily improve. Here is where women must rely on the support of one another, sharing frank discussion and body/sexuality affirming activities like dance or exercise. Although it may seem odd at first, singing with others is also good because it frees the heart and opens the throat. There is a recognised neuromuscular association between the mouth and the vagina: if one is tight, so will the other be.

In many cultures, ritual dance of some sort has been regularly practised by pregnant women. Contrary to popular belief, belly dancing was not developed to please and seduce men, but rather to support and reinforce the efforts of women in labour. The movements of the dance, the rolling of the hips and the undulation of the belly, tend to occur spontaneously during labour in women free of cultural inhibitions. Considering the discomfort and pain of the birth process, a circle of dancing women must have served to remind the mother how to let go, at the same time echoing her emotional and physical responses in a deeply bonding experience for all. Where, in today's institutionalised birthing system, might we find the privacy and support to do the same?

To return to the issue of mother/lover role conflict, it is important to add that some women feel this themselves, and may manifest it either by avoiding sex or by wanting to focus exclusively on the baby. Resulting problems may be considerable; disrupted intimacy in a rapidly changing relationship can breed distrust and estrangement unless communication lines are kept open. As a midwife, I use the sexual nature of the birth process as a reference point to encourage a woman to stay open as much as possible to her partner. I suggest she experiment with positions, such as being on top or lying on her side, that will give her more control over depth of penetration and rate of thrusting. Labour is, after all, an intensely physical experience; the estimated caloric output of the first birth is equivalent to that of a 50 mile hike! And it also involves the same kind of emotional surrender as spontaneous orgasm.

An important aside here about physical and/or sexual abuse: more and more women are becoming aware of forgotten or repressed experiences now that support and acceptance are forthcoming. And for many, the emotional vulnerability of pregnancy may trigger recollections for the first time that are doubly difficult to handle if your own parents or other relatives are implicated. Naturally, the accompanying sorrows and fears are apt to interfere with your primary relationship. But, wherever possible, it is better to bring these to the surface while pregnant than to have them arise and interfere with labour, or with mothering itself. Hypnosis can be especially useful for reactivating and healing the past, precisely because pregnancy is such a labile state.

Other psychological barriers to intimacy may involve anxieties about money, role changes, security, etc. Any woman who finds herself at a sexual impasse while pregnant should make every effort to find assistance.

Here's a relevant account from Mariann:

I went to a woman's psychotherapy conference while pregnant and took a workshop on sexual abuse. I didn't even know why I was there, really, just for the info, I thought. We went around the room with introductions and after the first few heart-wrenching accounts, I felt somewhat out of place. But after a time, I remembered something that happened to me as a child, something I'd completely blocked out. I guess I thought it was no big deal – I was fondled by a conductor on a train when I was 12 – but that day, I relived all of my shame and confusion. I learned that women often tend to minimise these experiences, even though they have considerable impact. Just being aware of what happened to me shed light on certain aspects of my personality and the way I am with sex. Being pregnant, I felt open enough to make some changes.

Again, as regards mid-pregnancy, no matter what a

woman's personal challenges, this is a fine time for integration, a time to find stability and prepare for the changes ahead.

## THE THIRD TRIMESTER

If the first trimester is viewed as initiation and the second as the point of equilibrium, then the third trimester is the phase of completion and overflow to the next cycle: that of labour and delivery. Sexuality can be disrupted at this stage by the natural physical discomforts of being so very pregnant and carrying so much extra weight. Sleep may be sporadic as comfortable positions become harder to find, although lying on your side with pillows between your legs and under the belly can help. If there is heartburn, caused by progesterone softening the oesophageal valve so that stomach acids rise upwards, a woman may find that the only way she can sleep is propped upright. And she may need to urinate several times nightly, due to increased pressure from the baby against the bladder. None of this is particularly conducive to *amour*, but the midday rendez-vous or other creative solutions may work. Also, pelvic cartilage is softened considerably by progesterone and oestrogen both, so that ordinary pressure on the pubic bone becomes uncomfortable. Many women long to feel their partners heavy on top of them, and dream of sleeping on their stomachs. It makes sense that these longings, combined with the inconvenience of interrupted sleep, promote a readiness to give up pregnancy and get on with labour, while simultaneously preparing a woman for the challenges of caring for the newborn baby.

Backache is another major complaint at this time, as the enlarged uterus greatly distends the abdominals and pulls the back out of alignment. Rocking the pelvis whilst on your hands and knees, standing or even sitting (while driving, for example) can help tremendously. Of course, pelvic rocking comes naturally during intercourse, as does increased circulation which can soothe and heal the lower back as well.

Emotionally, these are trying times, with mixed feelings over the sexual relationship. Sometimes a woman wants to cling to her partner and hold back time, well aware that the baby will soon be out in the world (or in the middle of the bed) and nothing will ever be quite the same again. Sometimes a woman wants privacy and solitude just to be with the baby, trying to get to know it as well as she can before it is born. Sex may seem extraneous, or more for her partner than for herself. Especially when she's thinking of the challenges ahead and her ongoing need for support, she may be demanding, moody, fearful. Other times, she'll feel fully confident, excited by the future and wanting to make love to her partner with happiness and abandon.

Hormones are at least partially responsible for this range of responses, because they are once again on the move, shifting around erratically in preparation for birth. Then, in the last week or so, a drop in progesterone as a precursor to labour often leads to a loss of water weight, a feeling of lightness, clarity and well-being. Increased levels of oestrogen may further contribute to mood elevation and new found energy. Other substances known as prostaglandins, which are fatty acids found in the brain, lungs, kidneys and prostate gland as well as in seminal and menstrual fluids, also increase at term and may be responsible for labour's onset. Or it may be the foetus that is responsible; it too releases prostaglandins as its brain matures. Whatever the source, prostaglandins are known to soften the cervix and cause uterine contractions. Although oxytocin also serves to stimulate uterine activity, it appears less critical in initiating labour and more important in promoting its progress.

This is why many doctors and midwives now encourage intercourse at term, especially if the baby is overdue. Seminal fluid is extremely high in prostaglandins, and thus may serve to trigger labour. (A substitute may be found in evening primrose oil; rubbed gently on the cervical area, it is reputed to have a similar effect, as a prostaglandin precursor.) Sheila Kitzinger, author of *Women's Experience of Sex* and numerous books on pregnancy, recommends a particular sexual technique for getting labour going. She advises a woman to make love on her back well supported by pillows under her hips, her partner kneeling between her legs. The woman then places, one at a time, her ankles on her partner's shoulders. This allows for the deepest possible penetration. After he ejaculates, she is to stay with hips elevated for at least fifteen minutes so that prostaglandins may be well absorbed by the cervix. Then follows nipple stimulation, at intervals of ten minutes or so, to stimulate oxytocin's release and subsequent uterine activity.

This technique replicates the current medical practice of using prostaglandin suppositories to 'ripen' the cervix, followed by intravenous syntocinon (synthetic oxytocin) drip to induce contractions. Given the choice, most women would probably choose the former, both to avoid the intrusion of technology and to enhance intimacy as labour begins.

## LABOUR AND BIRTH

As labour starts, pregnancy is ending. Many women feel genuine sadness at this, especially if it's to be the last baby or the pregnancy itself has been especially fulfilling. And some may feel trepidation due to the dawning awareness that the only way out of labour is through it. Fortunately, there is a classic burst of energy at labour's onset, due probably to a peak in oestrogen and the additional influence of oxytocin.

Is childbirth really a sexual event? How can this be, when it's reputed to be so painful? And if birth is sexual in the usual sense, then how do women cope in impersonal hospital settings, surrounded by relative strangers?

Let's consider these questions one at a time. Birth as a sexual event – really, who can doubt it? It is, after all, an intensely physical experience centred on a woman's genitals! During labour, the entire pelvic area is charged with energy: the vagina, clitoris, rectum, anus, and all supporting tissues and musculature. Women often associate the sensations of labour contractions with those of extremely strong menstrual cramps, but with one important difference. Contractions come in waves, building up steadily instead of taking hold abruptly. Women who have learned to cope with menstrual cramps by relaxing, staying loose, letting go, have a distinct advantage in labour. And here is where the parallels to sexual intercourse begin. Particularly when sex is very passionate and forceful, there may be moments of pain or cramping discomfort with deep thrusting and intense pelvic movement, particularly if the cervix is being hit directly or the uterus jolted against the intestines. Relaxation, rhythmic breathing and a change of position can help a woman ease through without losing energy, as she would if she tightened up or shut down emotionally. Especially with orgasm, the ability to surrender and diffuse sensation throughout the body is critical.

Deep relaxation, surrender, letting go: when midwives are asked to disclose the secret of giving birth harmoniously, these are the words we choose. Not merely as metaphor, but as physiological fact, as we will see in the coming section. We will also look closely at how environment affects the spontaneity of the birth process.

### FIRST STAGE LABOUR

The first stage is the phase of labour wherein the cervix dilates fully to allow the baby to begin its passage through the vagina, or birth canal, and out into the world. The cervical opening is ordinarily closed or stretchy only a fingertip's worth; now it will dilate to a circle of approximately ten centimetres in diameter. Just how this occurs will be explored in a moment; mostly it's a matter of oxytocin intensifying contractions and bringing them closer together.

But in early labour, up to about four centimetres of dilation, contractions may be scarcely noticeable or may feel more like waves of pelvic warmth 'with an edge' than painful cramping. So, how about making love in early labour? Considering the connection between sex and the release of oxytocin, this is really quite a good idea. A caution, though: most practitioners feel that vaginal penetration should be avoided once the waters have broken, lest infection occur. But generally, intercourse in early labour relaxes the pelvis, gets the hormones pumping and eases both partners into an intimate and relaxed state conducive to ready progress. Especially if labour is slow starting or long and drawn out in the early phase, sex may be just the thing. What's more, couples may find a dimension in lovemaking never before experienced. I've definitely learned my lesson about knocking before entering the labour room, particularly when attending home births. I can think of several times when couples hurriedly pulled clothes back on or grabbed a blanket, only to have me tell them to go right ahead!

Some women feel like staying just shy of orgasm; others do not. Celine reports, 'Just being close with our clothes off, being caressed, helped me relax a lot and take the contractions in stride. I don't know why, but kissing was especially good! Even though my partner eventually came inside me, I felt more like taking it easy than building up to orgasm.'

Kissing and letting go – remember the neuromuscular association between mouth and vagina? In her wonderful book, *Spiritual Midwifery*, Ina May Gaskin tells of one couple she directed to kiss in a certain way: the woman with her lips on top, spread out over her partner's. This led to a tangible shift in labour's intensity and very rapid progress. One of the classic lines from this book is the observation, 'The same energy that gets the baby in, gets the baby out.'

Still, no matter how well a woman has prepared and how eagerly anticipated her labour, there may come a time when the going gets rough, as sensations exceed her expectations. This is when ideas of what labour is to be like, concepts of coping and proper behaviour must be swept aside for the real thing. In that moment, women often find they must go further in letting go physically than they ever have before. This is what I call the point of reckoning, of realising that labour is bigger than you are, beyond your experience or control. Naturally, this is somewhat frightening, especially because it tends to occur fairly early, at just four or five centimetres' dilation. A woman may feel that she has already tried everything and is still not making it. Truth is, she's not going to make it or do it as her ordinary self, she must transform somehow to get through it. As you may surmise, this is also a time when women ask for drugs, particularly if they feel unsupported or exposed.

Imagine yourself struggling with physical sensations much stronger than expected, painful the second you tense up or break your concentration, yet the constant parade of nurses and doctors in and out of your room makes it nearly impossible to let go and relax. You find yourself afraid, wanting to cry out and find relief, move around and change positions, perhaps, but your circumstances are far too inhibiting. Your attendants are sympathetic and encouraging, but no one is really getting down to your level, looking you in the eye. Though your partner is standing by, he too feels afraid and helpless.

Niles Newton, a remarkable woman who has done much ground-breaking research on birth, breastfeeding and sexuality, investigated the importance of environmental factors on the birth of mice. She found that births were longer, more difficult and/or obstructed when the mice were placed in unfamiliar surroundings, could not smell or see what they were used to, were moved repeatedly during labour or were placed in clear cages (as opposed to opaque) so that privacy was absent. Opposite factors of familiar surroundings, privacy and stability contributed to spontaneous, easy deliveries.[3]

It was Grantly Dick-Read who first explained how fear or tension can cause pain and lack of progress in labour. The uterus is composed of several muscular layers, the outer with long fibres, the inner with circular fibres. In the absence of fear or tension, oxytocin works on the long fibres, causing them to contract, retract and become shorter. The inner muscle fibres (which encircle the cervix) stay soft and relaxed, and the shortening of the long fibres gradually pulls the cervix open. But when a woman is tense or frightened elevated adrenaline levels shunt blood away from the uterus to the extremities and cause the circular fibres of the uterus to become rigid. The two muscle layers then work in opposition so that pain results.[4] Similarly, if you are tense or frightened during intercourse, you're not likely to experience orgasm.

How to avoid all this? Picture yourself in a darkened room with just your partner, the two of you in bed or thereabouts, your midwife or doctor sitting quietly in the corner, coming over now and then to check the baby and offer encouragement but generally unobtrusive, perhaps retiring to an adjacent area so your privacy is complete. You still have to deal with the pain, both the physical intensity and the psychological trauma of, 'It's not what I expected.' But you can speak freely to your partner, you can cry, laugh, shout, whatever suits as you work together; it is your experience.

A major problem with hospital births is that increasingly there is routine intervention in otherwise normal labour. Once the decision is made for one intervention, others are likely to follow. For example, when syntocinon is used to speed up labour (as per general guidelines that dilation should proceed at a certain rate), contractions may become so unnaturally strong and painful that the mother requires pain relief or becomes less cooperative with the process. These ultra-strong contractions also place stress on the baby by pushing the uterus, which never relaxes completely enough to be well oxygenated. If foetal distress persists, as is likely since by now the mother is sedated and the uterus dependent on artificial stimulation, the probable conclusion is Caesarean delivery. Consider that one in five births today is by Caesarean section: in some hospitals, as many as one in three. This is shocking but not really surprising, considering how deeply our society venerates control. Some women even request Caesarean birth for much the same reason; it seems less threatening and easier to handle. Little do they know (nor are they told) how difficult recovery from surgery can be when one must tend a baby, establish breastfeeding, suffer sleep deprivation and deal with sweeping physiological and emotional changes.

Old medical texts teach that less than five per cent of births involve complications. Our 20–30 per cent Caesarean rate has, for the most part, iatrogenic causes, i.e., those generated by technology, procedure or practitioner. And all in the name of perfection and protection from the unknown (and from lawsuits). That birth is a mystery which can never be fully circumscribed by technology is a simple fact of life. Even in the most carefully monitored situations, haemorrhages occur unexpectedly, babies get stuck at the shoulder, cord accidents happen at the last minute, babies and mothers die. The bottom line, however, is that in spite of all our intervention, we have a *higher* perinatal mortality rate than most countries where birth occurs spontaneously and is commonly attended at home.

Whatever your environment, once you make the shift to active labour (contractions long and strong, coming about every five minutes), neurohormones called endorphins will begin to enter your bloodstream. Released during intense physical activity and responsible for the surge of strength, power and well-being known as the second wind, these are the same substances that cause 'runner's high'. Once the endorphins have kicked in, a woman may actually enjoy labour or may even find it ecstatic. I've told many times the story of one of my clients who was crying and desperate in early labour, only to be smiling and dancing around the room at nine centimetres' dilation. Not every woman can maintain an external focus so far into labour; it depends how strong contractions are and how quickly labour is progressing. Many turn inward, with eyes closed between contractions, apparently dozing or peacefully out of body. Still, there is always the exception, like the woman who laughed, chatted and ate fried chicken right up to full dilation!

Endorphins are also released during intercourse, and lead to the exquisite feeling known as afterglow. But if anaesthetics or analgesics are used in labour, stress perception will be minimal and endorphin release may not occur. Although pain may be nearly obliterated by medication, so too will the transcendental feeling many women report in giving birth naturally, particularly at the height of dilation.

What happens next? Even women who have never been pregnant have heard of the transition phase of labour, reputed to be the most difficult of all. Not every woman experiences transition, but for those that do, it occurs somewhere around eight to ten centimetres' dilation. Physically, the cervix continues to dilate even as the baby descends through it and pushes onto the pelvic floor. This leads to mixed, conflicting messages of 'Relax, stay open, surrender', and 'Ummm, push, bear down, get busy!' Just when a woman feels she has finally made her peace with letting go, she suddenly becomes compelled to do something, to act. Emotionally, her mood swings wildly; she may swear at her husband or birth attendants. Hormonally, there are ongoing rushes of oxytocin interspersed with surges of adrenaline.

But wait, you say. How can these purportedly conflicting hormones work in concert? According to Michel Odent, there comes a time (generally around the shift from first to second stage) when adrenaline is both physiological and positive in effect. He explains the paradoxical effects of adrenaline by identifying two different kinds of uterine receptors: beta-inhibitory and alpha-initiatory. Adrenaline is also a precursor to prostaglandin release (bringing to mind the characteristic burst of energy just before labour starts), and increased prostaglandin levels are thought to be responsible for the bearing-down reflex. Tying this physiology to animal behaviour in the wild, Odent notes that if threatened in early labour, a mother will be at an advantage if labour stops, but if labour is well advanced or happening quickly, it will be to her advantage to give birth as soon as possible.[5]

Odent further notes that the physiological release of adrenaline may be accompanied by surges of fear or anxiety. But is adrenaline a precursor to these emotions, or the other way around? In either case, at least if a woman experiences panic, she can feel comforted in knowing it is normal. She may even have mortal fear and feel as though she must fight for survival. She may well cry out or scream. This is in direct contradiction to what is taught in most childbirth preparation classes: that a woman should make only low-pitched sounds lest she tighten up, and should make the transition to second stage as calmly as possible. On the contrary, women left to their own spontaneous devices often scream or roar as they enter second stage, sometimes leaping to their feet or into a crouch with superhuman strength. These same women later revel in the power of this moment. 'Those sounds,' one recalled, 'where were they coming from? Some deep part of me that had never been touched before. They rang in my ears – raw, clear and unbelievably strong.' 'I felt so primal,' said another, 'like some sort of tigress, a jungle queen.' For many, this is one of the most sexual moments in giving birth, one that can transform a previously shy or inhibited woman into a powerfully assertive lover.

## SECOND STAGE LABOUR

To backtrack a bit, we must clarify that although second stage commences with full dilation, some women do not experience the adrenaline surge and urge to push for some time after, especially if the baby is still fairly high in the pelvis. Sometimes, if labour has been long or hard thus far, women even sleep or nap as the uterus rests, then wake with clear urges to push. As bearing-down signals get stronger, pressure begins to build in the vagina. What is this sensation like? Imagine an object the size of grapefruit (the baby's head) pressing on all the sensitive areas deep inside you, combined with a downward squeezing urge something like moving your bowels but multiplied ten times – a whole body urge, almost like turning inside out, and you have some idea of the sensory magnitude as delivery approaches. No wonder we need a burst of adrenaline to help us through! Physiologically, the uterus has stretched and thinned in the lower segment while the long fibres have retracted to form a mass at the top, which then pushes the baby downwards. And it is primarily the uterus that pushes the baby out, not the mother, although her ability to cooperate with her body makes a difference in ease of progress. Second stage can be 20 minutes of urges so overwhelming that a woman can scarcely catch her breath, or may last several hours with urges of varying length and intensity, sometimes so light she can breathe right through them.

Once again, however, we find medical management at odds with basic physiology; labour and delivery staff seem determined in nearly every case to get the baby out as soon as possible. Women are told to draw their legs back forcibly, hold a breath as long as possible and push their guts out with every contraction. This is rather like trying to force orgasm, riding over the rhythm instead of with it. To put it another way: under which circumstances might you find it easier to have an orgasm, with someone barking orders at you every step of the way, or when free to surrender your body and let it take you? Most probably, aggressive management of second stage is a remnant of the old notion that it is dangerous for both mother and baby to let the foetal head 'pound the perineum'. If anything, forced and insensitive pushing is apt to cause damage to vaginal tissues, at the same time depriving the baby of oxygen. As demonstrated by Roberto Caldeyro-Barcia, unnaturally long periods of maternal breath-holding can lead to foetal acidosis and distress.[6] Sheila Kitzinger goes so far as to say that the problem is that of imposing a male ejaculation model on the pushing process, for which the variable-intensity, multiply-orgasmic feminine model is imminently more suitable.

When a woman in second stage is unfettered by outside direction she will, in fact, breathe very much as she would during sexual excitation and orgasm: up to three times more rapidly than usual, with periods of breath-holding punctuated by gasps, groans or cries. Women allowed to push their babies out spontaneously do describe delivery in sexual terms, speaking of tremendous release, ecstatic rushes of emotion, overwhelming happiness, and so on. I've observed that if women are controlled by others while pushing, they are somewhat inhibited at first with their babies.

For me, the ecstasy of second stage occurred when my uterus and I were working as one, beyond signal and response. In this mode, a woman can literally deliver her own baby, sensing exactly when she can take more stretch and when to ease up, effortlessly breathing her baby out. After a huge episiotomy (cut to enlarge the birth canal) with my first child, I was determined not to tear with my second, so I really tuned in during pushing, just closed my eyes and did it all from the inside. I could feel *everything*, the precise contours of my daughter's head as I eased it out, even her little shoulders and body as she whooshed and squiggled through. It was absolutely the most exquisite thing I have ever felt in my life. Later, my midwives said they wished they had the birth on tape, it was so perfectly controlled. But that's not the way I would describe my process, as I wasn't really holding back. Beyond attunement, there was union, perfect union.

There has been some interesting research regarding vaginal stimulation in labour and subsequent bonding behaviours. Vaginal stimulation has been shown to be an important determinant of bonding in sheep.[7] When vaginal stimulation by vibrator was given to non-pregnant ewes primed with oestrogen and progesterone, they responded to newborn lambs with a full range of bonding behaviour. With similar stimulation, recently delivered ewes already bonded to their own lambs stopped rejective behaviour to alien lambs and accepted them as their own. Further, Krehbiel and co-workers (1982)[8] found that by giving peridural anaesthetics to ewes during labour, particularly if given early, maternal behaviour was severely altered; seven of the eight first-time mothers failed to show any normal bonding behaviour during the first half hour. Animals that had given birth before responded less noticeably, but still showed some effects. Perhaps the choice of epidural anaesthesia (which numbs to a greater extent than does peridural) is not so benign as we've thought. I've noticed that once an epidural is administered, a woman becomes more a spectator than a participant, although epidurals in low doses to aid in the event of obstruction can sometimes make the difference between vaginal birth and Caesarean section.

All of this raises yet another issue, that of vaginal tearing with delivery. Isn't it better to have an episiotomy, rather than being stretched out or torn? And if an episiotomy is going to be necessary, then mustn't the area be numbed in advance anyway?

Here we have one of the biggest lies perpetuated by modern obstetrics: that the human vagina is somehow inadequate to the task of delivery and must be surgically enhanced. Most women don't realise that the surface of the vagina is covered with ruggae, accordion-like folds of tissue which naturally expand under the hormonal influence of parturition. When a woman is relaxed and centred during the delivery, not rushed but well supported, she will generally give birth without a nick (or with abrasions so minor they require no treatment). And despite beliefs to the contrary, nice clean episiotomy cuts are not easier to heal than tears that do require stitches. The irregular edges of a tear actually mesh together better and close more quickly. Finally, it is much easier to regain sexual pleasure and muscle response after repair of a tear than an episiotomy. Tears frequently skim the surface, but in doing an episiotomy one is obliged to cut through muscle. The end result is a wall of scar tissue both inflexible and numb to sensation.

But what about overall snugness, you may wonder? How can an area that has been stretched so completely ever regain its former tone? And isn't that what the 'husband's stitch' is for? Theoretically, yes – but that final excessively tight stitch is external, right at the base of the vaginal opening, and does little more than cause pain and distress with intercourse. Pleasurable friction comes not at the opening but from muscles immediately inside the vagina, which extend upwards several inches or so. Although it is possible to create a tight vaginal opening with surgical repair, scarred areas inside will be rigid, surrounding muscles flaccid and the entire area dysfunctional for quite some time. When the vagina is intact, however, the muscles continue to respond as a unit. A woman who is well aroused naturally tightens at the opening and just inside, while the back portion of the vaginal canal balloons several inches longer and wider (nature's design to allow seminal fluid to pool around the cervix). In general, a woman who has given birth naturally and has retoned her vaginal muscles will be more responsive and pleasurable a partner than one with deep tissue trauma and repair (at least, until the healing occurs, which can take many months).

In the 1950s, when the 'husband's knot' became a standard part of repair technique, women were not taught pelvic floor exercises (detailed in Chapter Four) and few explored their own musculature for fear of hurting themselves or doing something 'dirty'. Sexual mores were based on male gratification; little was known or understood about female sexual response. Times have changed, women are more in possession of their own bodies and most have no qualms about putting fingers into the vagina to aid them in toning the muscles there. In fact, women who are in touch with themselves this way and who have been prepared to give birth without an episiotomy but, at the last minute, are given one anyway, often feel violated and emotionally traumatised. As one woman, Jan, recalled of her first birth, 'I felt I was doing a good job, easing my baby out nicely, when suddenly and for no apparent reason my doctor changed his mind and cut me. I felt like, 'Oh ... well, okay, I give up ... guess I'm not good enough.' I lost all feeling, and he took control.' In over 300 deliveries, I've had to perform episiotomy only five times, due to last minute foetal distress necessitating immediate delivery. And I've had very few women tear. My secrets: engage the woman in sensitive breathing, use hot compresses and perineal massage, and help her to take it slowly.

## DELIVERY

At the final moment of crowning, when the widest part of the head stretches the vaginal opening to its maximum, some women love either to look in a mirror or to reach down and feel, for the first time, their little one. Sometimes this brings an overwhelming flood of emotion, and the baby is born in an orgasm of delivery. Women describe the moment of delivery as the high point of their lives, a pinnacle emotionally and physically. All the waiting and wondering, all the hopes and fears are finally unleashed and allowed to rush forward as the baby swooshes out and utters its first cry.

If she feels like it, the mother can reach down and lift the baby up when it is still partly inside her: something she will never forget. The baby is wet, warm, incredibly fragile yet surprisingly strong. It smells sweetly of birth. She touches its little hands and feet, and then finds herself falling into its eyes, seeing the faces of relatives and ancestors, feeling past and future unite simultaneously. Birth is a stunning and overwhelming victory for a woman, especially when she has retained her power and knows she has given it her all.

In the next chapter, we will explore the tender and tempestuous postpartum period, and look at how sexual identity and self-expression are affected and transformed by the presence of a newborn.

1. Davis, Elizabeth, *Energetic Pregnancy* (Berkeley, California, Celestial Arts, 1988)
2. Newton, Niles, and Modahl, Charlotte, 'New Frontiers of Oxytocin Research', *Free Woman: Women's Health in the 1990s* (Canforth, Pantheon Publishing Group, 1989)
3. Newton, Niles, Newton, Michael and Foshee, Donald, Experimental Inhibition of Labor Through Environmental Disturbance',

*Obstetrics and Gynecology* (Vol. 27, 1966)

4. Dick-Read, Grantly, *Childbirth Without Fear* (New York, Harper & Row, 1959)

5. Odent, Michel, *Water and Sexuality* (London, Penguin Books, 1990)

6. Caldeyro-Barcia, Roberto, 'The Influence of Maternal Bearing-down Efforts During Second Stage on Fetal Well-being', *Birth and the Family Journal* (Vol. 6:1, Spring 1979)

7. Keverne, E.B., Levy, F., Poindron, P., Lindsay, D.R., 'Vaginal Stimulation: An Important Determinant of Maternal Bonding in Sheep', *Science* (Vol. 219, 1983)

8. Krehbiel, D., Poindron, P., Levy, F., Podhomme, M.J., 'Peridural Anesthesia Disturbs Maternal Behavior in Primiparous and Multi-parous Parturient Ewes', *Physiology and Behavior* (Vol. 40, 1982)

# 4

# Sex after the baby comes

The postpartum period, defined as a minimum of six weeks and a maximum of three years following birth, is undoubtedly one of the most tempestuous and challenging phases of a woman's life. It's been said that the relative pleasure and exhilaration of pregnancy and birth are but preparation for the gruelling adjustments postpartum. I often tell women that the first six weeks of caring for a newborn baby is the hardest work they will ever do. The changes that must be made in adding another member to the family group and in altering the household routine are far from minor. The stress of it all may well lead a woman to wonder whether there is sex after birth.

## THE RECOVERY PROCESS

With a little patience and creativity, sex usually comes back better than ever, even though modifications will be called for. But to truly understand sexuality during this phase, we must first look at the physical process of recovery as well as that of lactation.

In the first few moments following delivery, fresh spurts of oxytocin are released to contract the uterus and shear off the placenta. As the baby is put to the breast, nipple stimulation triggers additional oxytocin which shrinks the uterus down to the size of a grapefruit. Over the next ten days or so, continued release of oxytocin will contract the uterus back to its pre-pregnant size. When a woman breastfeeds, oxytocin levels rise even higher according to frequency of nursing, which in the first few weeks may occur as often as every hour or two. The extra boost serves to contract and tone the upper vaginal area (or vault), a process which takes place much more slowly in women who bottle-feed.

Breastfeeding is initiated in part by the hormone pro-lactin, which is released as oestrogen and progesterone levels drop with delivery. Ongoing milk production is due to sucking stimulation of the breasts; the more the baby sucks, the more milk the mother will produce, provided she has adequate rest, food and drink.

The let-down of milk is caused by oxytocin's release, most directly by nipple stimulation. But let-down of milk may occur in other ways; women often report that hearing their baby cry (or any baby, if they are in a public place) will bring the milk down and dripping. Others find that just thinking about the baby will fill their breasts. Similarly, a woman overwhelmed with love and passion for her partner may have an orgasm the moment she is entered, with very little physical stimulation. Again, we see how closely oxytocin levels are connected to emotional states.

What does let-down feel like? Generally, it's very pleasurable. There is a tingling in the breasts, a tightening as they fill, and a longing for release. We have, I think, a ready correlation to what men experience with arousal. There is definitely an urgency to find a partner: a mother experiencing let-down really *wants* her baby. No wonder women find breastfeeting to be a sexual experience! Sometimes, the accompanying uterine and vaginal contractions even lead to orgasm. At the very least, unless a woman has overriding inhibitions, breastfeeding is physically satisfying and fulfilling. There is a characteristic feeling of warmth and well-being that encompasses body and soul: a flow of energy that is soothing and healing. And it is a shared experience. The baby responds with love and desire; its little hands stroke the breast, its body presses forward (as it gets older) and its toes may curl rhythmically. Just as sexual intercourse bonds emotionally healthy adults together, so does breastfeeding bond mother and child. We're little accustomed to thinking of babies (or children) as having sexual needs, but to a certain extent, they do. Close to our most basic definition of sexual desire is the physical and emotional urge for intimacy that is with us from birth.

Niles Newton and Charlotte Modahl found that mood changes caused by breastfeeding are very much like those that occur with intercourse and orgasm. On the other hand, women who bottle-feed their babies have been shown to have higher levels of depression, anxiety, stress, regression, and guilt on a day-to-day basis than mothers who breastfeed.[1] According to the research of E. B. Thoman and co-workers, lactating women have shown a suppression of adrenaline release and accompanying neurological activity in response to various kinds of trauma.[2] It would seem that the release of oxytocin through breast-feeding is something of a biological perk to help women buffer stress and make it through the physical challenges of this phase, such as sleep deprivation, hormonally-based emotional changes and sweeping physiological adjustments.

Postpartum adjustment is indeed more than a matter of restoring pelvic anatomy and establishing breastfeeding. Remember the changes of pregnancy: elevated blood volume, increased thyroid and kidney function, decreases in vascular tension, changes in digestion, etc. In the first few weeks postpartum, all these shift back to normal. This is not a smooth, even process of change but an erratic and fitful one. Hormones ebb, flow and intricately readjust. The resulting hot flushes and cold spells, night sweats and mood swings lead this to be a biologically and emotionally charged period for women and their families.

## EMOTIONAL CHANGE AND ADJUSTMENT

Distinguishing the biologically-induced mood swings of this period from those based on more far reaching socio-emotional concerns is a real challenge, especially for women going it alone. To treat the new mother as though nothing has changed, and expect that she will be back on her feet and in charge of her affairs in a matter of days is the height of denial, considering the monumental task of adjusting to a new way of life. And what is she to think, alone at home in the midst of total turmoil, except that she is weak, incompetent or totally out of her mind? In many cultures some observation is made of the lying-in period, a time when women are expected to rest and recover. Sometimes this lasts six weeks, sometimes only ten days, but in any case, there is acknowledgement of the mother's need to be cared for completely in order that she may care well for another. Care of new mothers ensures survival of the species, but more than that, it ultimately affects both quality of life and culture. A well-supported and confident mother will bond better, love more deeply and be better able to distinguish her own needs from those of her child.

Good care frees her to continue to develop as an individual, giving her a healthy foundation on which to base her social interactions and contributions to society. And her child will reap the benefits of security and integrity in its own process of development.

Often, postpartum customs in Native American and Indonesian cultures involve the use of heat, either heating the room or building a fire near or under the mother's bed so she may be unclothed, nurse spontaneously, feel relaxed and at ease. Far from the overwhelming isolation new mothers experience in the so-called developed world, she is surrounded by her peers and extended family, women who are knowledgeable and loving. They feed her, laugh with her, counsel her, marvel at the miracle of her newborn child. In many ways, the mother is being mothered so that she may learn attitude and technique. In the Philippines, the new mother is considered to be in such a state of vulnerability and grace that should she die in the first 40 days postpartum, her soul will automatically go to heaven.

When a woman is not well cared for at this time, there are complex, often long-term effects on her body, personality and sexuality. Even though we've noted oxytocin's ability to buffer stress, there are definitely limits. If a woman is forced out of bed or back to work too soon, overproduction of adrenaline will severely inhibit recovery. As Newton states, 'Oxytocin reflexes can be severely inhibited by environmental disturbances, emotional upset or pain.'[3] What this really means is that the Amazon concept of postpartum recovery is mostly myth: women are *not* intended to give birth in the bushes and jump back on their horses. The notoriously high incidence of postpartum depression in the United States has frustrated biological needs at its root. Without adequate rest, recuperation is gruelling and prolonged, and sex is the last thing on a woman's mind.

But there are other factors, too. The same cultural ideology that deems it appropriate to abandon new mothers, further challenges a woman's identity. After all, the new mother is a new person. In our society, she will experience definite losses as she takes on her new role. For example, single friends may abandon her, finding it impossible to relate to what she and her family are experiencing. Her primary relationship is altered and may become somewhat strained. She herself is inextricably changed; her old routines and ways of handling daily business are in total upheaval. Privacy seems a thing of the past, at least at the beginning.

On a practical level, she will experience a loss of income if she takes maternity leave, with a probable drop in her standard of living. More significantly, her temporary loss of energy and resourcefulness may seem all but permanent unless she receives assistance. Chronic fatigue – really very common postpartum – may link to other losses and lead to depression. Women in this phase are fragile, vulnerable, impressionable and still quite sensitive from giving birth. Well-meaning but misguided advice sinks deep; criticism is not easily forgotten.

More than anything else, giving birth brings home the fact that control of life is just an illusion. Hopefully, a woman has a positive and exhilarating experience in making this discovery; if not, her self-esteem may be seriously damaged. This too can lead to lingering depression, particularly when combined with other postpartum stresses. One of my primary tasks as a midwife is to do postpartum home visits to see how my clients are healing and adjusting. Women often raise questions and express anxiety about their 'performance' or behaviour during the birth as early as day three, and sometimes call in tearful panic during the weeks that follow for more discussion, more reassurance. Of course, this is particularly true if the birth has been difficult, or the outcome somehow disappointing. Certainly the course of acceptance will be rocky if there are problems with the baby's health or physical condition. But a woman can have a perfectly beautiful and healthy baby and still be devastated by how birth went for her. Until very recently, women were denied the right to grieve over their own experience; as my mother was told when she complained to her doctor about the indignities she suffered at the hands of hospital staff, 'If the cake is good, eat it!' She told me this just days after my own traumatic first delivery, and it remains one of the pivotal moments in my life when I said to myself, 'No, this is not enough, I am worth more than that, *women* are worth more than that!'

Yet another aspect in a woman's recovery has to do with how well she has bonded to her baby. Much research has been done in this area, most of it showing damaging effects if mother and baby are separated for more than a few minutes during the first few hours, especially right at birth. Animals thus separated respond in classic ways: the newborn creature will bond with whatever is available (even another species, or something mechanical) and the mother will reject her young if later reintroduced. This is powerful genetic programming meant to ensure survival and when it is disrupted in the human sphere a woman feels herself rather like Humpty Dumpty: who can put the pieces back together again? Beyond immediate bonding, if a woman stays in the hospital for any time at all, nurses may feel obliged or may choose to begin caring for the baby: dressing it, changing its nappies, comforting it. But all of these are critical tasks that the mother needs to experience herself in order to develop maternal instinct and her own foundation for caregiving.

It is both curious and disappointing that in her most recent book, *Revolution From Within*, Gloria Steinem traces damage to self-esteem only so far back as the early years. She acknowledges that, 'As infants and small children, we cannot possibly earn our welcome in this world,'[4] but fails to link this to experience at birth. She also stresses the importance of 'honoring the wisdom of the body', yet seems unaware of how deeply this wisdom can be violated by birth trauma, and how devastating the effect on self-esteem. Indeed, if birth has been emotionally traumatic and bonding was disrupted, a chain reaction of missed communications and ineffective behaviour between mother and baby may make efforts to improve the relationship in the early years frustrating and exceedingly difficult.

And now it is time to tie all this to postpartum sexuality. At the most basic level, the key to sexual health and happiness in this phase has to do with the mother recognising her new self, working out her birth experience and accepting her changed role, then deepening her attachment to her baby. If she is able to do this, she will generally return to her partner with great enthusiasm. There are certain practical considerations regarding sex at this time, but ultimately, sex postpartum is not about timing and technique any more than it is at any other phase of a woman's life. The reason that many guidebooks take this focus is that identifying and dealing with the underlying issues is intimidating, to say the least. But if all we can offer a new mother concerned about her sexual identity is advice to do it in the afternoon when the baby sleeps, she is apt to feel like even her sex life has been pared down to practicality; that it, too, was lost when she gave birth.

There is, in fact, evidence that a good bond between

mother and baby makes for better sex. Masters and Johnson found that breastfeeding women had a higher level of sexual interest than bottle-feeding mothers. They were also, as a group, more interested in as rapid a return as possible to sexual activity with their partners.[5]

Breastfeeding provides, for many women, an important way to re-establish bonds that have been broken by difficult birth. Counselling is increasingly available for women who recognise their need for help in this area. And in spite of the crucial importance of bonding at birth, we human females are distinct from other mammals in that we have the intelligence and reason deliberately to recreate our bonds with others, including our young. This is far from easy or comfortable, but it definitely can be done.

## PRACTICALITIES OF POSTPARTUM SEX

Now we are ready to discuss the brass tacks of postpartum sexuality. Especially at first, women are greatly concerned for their internal healing and vulnerability during intercourse, particularly if they've had stitches.

Fear is often triggered by either pain or stiffness in the area that was stitched. Most doctors have women return for a checkup at about six weeks postpartum to determine degree of recovery, readiness for intercourse and appropriate contraception. But many women are told little or nothing of how to care for the perineum in the interim, nor such things to watch for as swelling, inflammation and signs of infection. Pain as a signal for attention may go unnoticed if a woman is taking painkillers during the first few days (the most critical time for healing).

For the record, I suggest that women use ice-packs for the first day or so to reduce swelling, then switch to sitz baths several times a day using hot water with selected herbs. Nothing speeds healing faster than heat, and soaking is far superior to topical application when it comes to stimulating circulation. Fresh ginger can be added to the soaking solution to relieve the itching which often occurs as stitches dissolve and skin heals. Grate the root (a three or four inch root will do fine) into a large pot of water, simmer 20 minutes, strain, and divide into two portions. Save one for later in the day, and dilute the first with water in the sitz bath unit (a special plastic tub which fits directly over the toilet seat, readily available at most hardware stores). After soaking for 20 minutes or so, thoroughly dry the perineum and leave exposed to air or sunlight another ten minutes before putting on a fresh pad (use a hair dryer to speed the process). If the area feels at all sticky, aloe vera gel will dry and soothe the tissues. Avoid vitamin E or other oil-based ointments until the skin is healed over, as these tend to keep edges from closing.

Despite the six-week ban on sex, some women go ahead and have it anyway before returning to their practitioner for the official okay. Sometimes this is fine; then again, the experience may be so fraught with anxiety and not a little pain that it is both worrisome and disappointing. Why the time limit at all? Ordinarily, it takes about ten days for the uterus to return to normal size and the cervix to close securely. If a woman has sex before then, she may notice bleeding beyond the normal lochia flow and she may also be at risk of uterine infection, although this has never been well documented. If she has had stitches, these will take a week or two to dissolve and at least two more to heal completely. A woman who has had stitches really should be checked before having sex, even if it means scheduling an appointment earlier than her practitioner expects or recommends.

Other women are so anxious about 'the first time' that

even the official all-clear is not enough. In this case, preliminary self-massage can help, particularly in areas with scar tissue. The wall-like ridge characteristic of episiotomy can be softened and relaxed by thumb or finger pressure, using a little oil (make sure to wash your hands before handling the baby or breastfeeding). When scarring is particularly extensive, evening primrose oil (found in healthfood shops) can make a noticeable difference. Due to a decrease in oestrogen postpartum, lack of vaginal lubrication poses a definite problem during sex. Water-based lubricating jelly is best for intercourse, as excess oil can clog delicate vaginal tissues and glands.

Oestrogen production will increase spontaneously if a mother stops nursing, or may resume gradually as she introduces solid foods and the baby nurses less often. There are exceptions, though. Some women nurse their babies (or even toddlers) just once or twice a day and still do not resume their normal cycles. Others may nurse exclusively and have milk in abundance, yet start menstruating as early as six weeks postpartum. The reasons for this discrepancy are uncertain. A number of my clients have observed that early sexual activity (within the first two weeks postpartum) seemed to cause them to start menstruating within the following month or two. No harm in this; certainly, a woman's sex life will benefit. But babies tend to be fussier when their mothers are menstruating, and women themselves may experience a struggle of their own with PMS, brought on by sleep deprivation and general fatigue. Although coping on these days is something of a strain, oestrogen's return serves to compensate.

If adequately repaired and cared for, the perineum should be fully healed after six weeks no matter how extensive the damage. I recently saw a woman who had been suffering for seven months with pain and bleeding during intercourse. She had been back to see her doctor, who offered little advice or assistance. Unfortunately, he was also a relative, so she hesitated to seek a second opinion lest word get back to him. As I suspected, she had been sewn up too tightly (the so-called 'husband's stitch'). Even with gentle pressure to the area, drops of blood appeared as the skin tore ever so slightly apart. She and her partner were quite frustrated and miserable. Ultimately, she had to go in for reconstructive surgery.

Bleeding without pain is normal for up to six weeks, but should be fairly light from about the third week on. It may increase temporarily with intense physical activity, indicating the need for more rest. The first intercourse may also cause a bit more bleeding; this is perfectly normal. But if bleeding persists past six weeks, placental fragments may be retained, or the endometrium over-proliferating. If there is any doubt, it's best to see a doctor.

A major concern women have about resuming sex is whether or not they will still be satisfactory in bed; whether there will be adequate tone in the vaginal muscles to bring the accustomed pleasure. Usually, some tone is lost at delivery, although breastfeeding naturally helps to restore it. And pelvic floor exercises can be started as early as day one. These aren't particularly easy at first (it is hard enough just to remember to do them), but often they feel more natural and effective if done while breastfeeding. There are two basic movements: one, a longitudinal stroking motion within the vagina as if one were caressing a soft fruit and squeezing out the juice; the other, a quick, snapping movement lower down, near the vaginal opening. These should feel challenging but stimulating and pleasurable. And there is nothing wrong with putting fingers inside to check effectiveness and progress. The use of these movements is actually part of both Tantric and Kundalini

*New Mother*

A week after our child was born,
you cornered me in the spare room
and we sank down on the bed.
You kissed me and kissed me, my milk undid its
burning slip-knot through my nipples,
soaking my shirt. All week I had smelled of milk,
fresh milk, sour. I began to throb:
my sex had been torn easily as cloth by the
crown of her head, I'd been cut with a knife and
sewn, the stitches pulling at my skin—
and the first time you're broken, you don't know
you'll be healed again, better than before.
I lay in fear and blood and milk
while you kissed and kissed me, your lips hot and swollen
as a teen-age boy's, your sex dry and big,
all of you so tender, you hung over me,
over the nest of the stitches, over the
splitting and tearing, with the patience of someone who
finds a wounded animal in the woods
and stays with it, not leaving its side
until it is whole, until it can run again.

From *The Dead and the Living*, by Sharon Olds, published by
Alfred Knopf, New York, 1984

traditions whereby women trigger the flow of energy up the
spine and throughout the body to enliven awareness and
promote well-being. These movements also occur naturally
with orgasm, thus sex itself is a great way to retone the
vagina.

Here are several accounts of first sex postpartum that
serve to illustrate both the awkwardness and transformation possible at this time. First from Tessa:

We had been through so much with the birth, John and I, which we planned for home but ended up having in the hospital. There were complications, for me and the baby, but I managed to [give] birth without needing a Caesarean. Then we had to stay in the hospital because of concerns for our son, and my husband was totally drawn into caring for us both. He was down in the nursery when they needed to do tests, talking to the staff, protecting the baby and bringing him right back to me. When we got home we were utterly exhausted, but that very night we made love. I knew I shouldn't (it was only the third day), but we couldn't help it, we had to unite, the urge was irresistible. It was, I think, the most intimate, powerful and explosive sex we've ever had. It just burst from both of us – we had been so close in pregnancy, and we really reached deep for each other, to get back to ourselves and heal what happened with the birth. I had a little bleeding after, but it was worth it. I'll never forget it.

And from Christine:

I waited a full four weeks, but Jarred was at his limit. I hadn't been to the doctor yet, but I'd been looking in a mirror and feeling around, and everything seemed fine. Well, when he entered me it felt so different that I think it shocked us both. The part that had stitches felt numb and stiff, and the rest of me felt all loose and out of control. But Jarred kept saying I felt so good, so warm, so soft that I put my fears aside and let myself go. When I came, milk started spurting from my breasts, and the baby started crying like it somehow got the signal. I went to get the baby and brought it into bed to nurse while Jarred licked milk from the other nipple – not exactly what I'd expected, but pretty satisfying all in all.

Leaking milk, by the way, is normal with orgasm since the natural release of oxytocin triggers let-down. It has also been noted that the hormone prolactin tends to synchronise mother/infant sleeping cycles, causing a sort of physiological empathy between the two.

This brings us to yet another area of concern, that of sleeping arrangements for the baby. In the last few decades, family sleeping (baby or children in bed with the parents) has seen a surge of popularity. Reports from those who have tried this are basically positive but somewhat mixed. At least in the beginning, having the baby in bed can help the mother get more sleep; often she will be able to nurse without fully awakening (the risk of rolling on top of the baby has proven to be nothing more than myth.) And increased skin-to-skin intimacy has emotional benefits for both parents and child. However, if it gets to the point where dad is off sleeping in a separate bed, it's time to reconsider the arrangement.

A wise paediatrician colleague suggests putting the baby in its own cot right next to the parents for at least part of the night, right from the beginning. This may help the baby get used to sleeping alone, at least part-time. One mother told me that when she and her husband decided to move their daughter's cot into a separate room, their little girl suddenly began sleeping through the night. (Apparently she had been disturbed by her parents' noises.) Not that sleeping all night in solitude is common for most little ones; children as old as five or six may still get into their parents' bed in the wee hours of the morning.

So how does this work in terms of sex? It depends on the age of the child; if yours is still an infant and you find yourself interrupted in the middle of something sweet, you can probably continue and get away with it. Many women report the stop-gap solution of nursing the baby while making love: an odd juggle of maternal and passionate emotions, but ultimately practical.

When the infant turns toddler, he or she will be too aware for this sort of thing. Still, be sure to let your little one see you and your partner cosily together, hugging and kissing, lest this behaviour lead to anxiety should he come upon you unawares. Of course, any child will be less jealous and possessive if regularly given lots of love and affection.

Ultimately, new parents make do. And they become creative, seeking out other times and places for intimate rendezvous. See the forthcoming section, 'Recapturing Intimacy', for further suggestions.

## SEXUAL INHIBITION AND DYSFUNCTION

Sometimes, sexuality is affected by more than practical concerns or typical adjustments. We've discussed already how sleep deprivation and lack of support can lead to transitory depression; if there are serious setbacks in recuperation or traumatic events such as death in the family, loss of a job or an unexpected move, loss of libido can easily occur.

And there may be deep-seated ambivalence about sexual roles and identity on the father's part. For a man who has been secretly harbouring the double standard (madonna/ whore) view of women, now may be the time when this can no longer be concealed. A man well able to love his partner passionately through pregnancy and birth may feel deeply uncomfortable in relating to her as a mother. She may notice that he seems hesitant to touch her, and think it's because she has lost her looks, is too stretched out inside or is no longer sexually enticing. But no, this is programming that many men are challenged to handle at this point. Some do so by having affairs, sad to say, while others plunge into their work or other outside efforts. Either way, it's no good for the marriage, and some sort of intervention is called for. Bear in mind that the postpartum period may be one of the first and most critical turning points for a man in reviewing misogynist thinking. There is nothing easy about this process, but it can lead in the long run to genuine co-parenting and more egalitarian and intimate ways of living and loving.

For her own part, a woman may also feel inhibited from time to time as she struggles with conflicts over her roles of mother, lover, and career woman. As long as she reassures her partner that these are her concerns and have nothing to do with his or her adequacy, they'll be much better off. It's all a matter of setting boundaries – something of a taboo for women in this culture. But personal boundaries are crucial to one's sanity, self-esteem and development. Under changed circumstances, as in the postpartum period, new boundaries must be established. New mothers have tremendous need to conserve energy, muster strength repeatedly and say no to anything that conflicts with their instincts. Setting boundaries means being straightforward and assertive, not holding back. Key phrases include, 'I can't', 'Could you?', 'No, not right now', 'Could we talk about it later?', and finally, 'I need to get some rest.'

In the same vein, it is important to be realistic about sex in this phase: it's not going to be like it was before. How could it be with constant interruptions, fatigue, the stress of making do (if only temporarily) with one income, or the opposite stress of being separated from the baby if both parents feel they must work? Let's face it – this is not one of those honeymoon times in a couple's life when sex is a breeze. This needn't cause panic if you take the broader view. That is what marriage/partnership is all about: the long-term view. It is great to be able to get it together enough to initiate new life, but that is just the beginning. When we start having sex to learn and grow, when we can engage without expectation and with the maturity to take from sex whatever we find, we have entered another stage of sexual development. Postpartum naturally initiates this evolution.

## RECAPTURING INTIMACY

Ideally, intimacy is not interrupted or in any way lost in the process of giving birth. But there is change, as we've discussed, and sometimes a couple must work to re-establish closeness and trust. This means talking about sex, communicating hurt, fears and desires more openly than ever. With a baby around, it also means making the effort to be emotionally and sexually available to one another, even when not fully in the mood. It means picking up wherever the two of you left off, even though days may intervene, keeping closeness in heart and deed.

Sylvia reports:

I felt very estranged from my body and so tired all the time I didn't want sex at all. Mark, on the other hand, would put pressure on me. Then I'd get in the mood, and he'd be too tired or something. Finally, I got in the habit of shutting him out, until one day he actually broke down and told me how much he missed me, missed our closeness. Really, I had forgotten that he cared, that I cared. The birth just turned me upside down, I guess, and I was so involved with the baby.

I told him what it was like for me, how exhausted and

used up I felt, and as we talked, one thing led to another and we were making love. It sure wasn't perfect (the baby actually interrupted with a nursing) but it was *real*. You know that quality, when sex is ultra-real? It was raw, it was different, it was new – we were three now, instead of two, more instead of less. Once I saw this, staying connected to Mark became easier. We got really good at blending sex into ordinary, day-to-day things we did, so that when we were alone, we got intimate quite quickly. I felt like I had discovered some secret to happy marriage and wondered, 'How come no one ever told me about this?'

Here are a few well-seasoned tips for keeping the fires burning:

1. **Have some ritual in your sex life.** Choose a night once a week to have dinner, wine, and a video after the baby is asleep, then have sex right there on the floor, on the couch, in the spare bed or wherever takes your fancy. Even if you are interrupted and can't resume, you know another special evening is only a week away.

2. **Get out.** Find a good babysitter willing to commit herself to a certain night each week. Choose someone you know and trust or seek recommendations from friends. It makes a difference to go out on a regular basis: the benefits build up. Once out, you'll tend to talk mostly about the baby, but try to talk about yourselves, too.

3. **Make cooking and housework as easy as possible.** If you ever planned to treat yourself to hired help, now is definitely the time. Buy a slow cooker, Dutch oven or

microwave for meals that practically cook themselves. Many birth practitioners recommend that a pregnant woman line up dinner preparation for the first week's postpartum from all those who have offered assistance (particularly if they want to come and see the baby). Or, you can cook casseroles, soups, etc., in advance and freeze as much as possible.

4. **Develop a sense of humour.** If you don't have one already, you'll definitely need it in the years ahead. Let your troubles roll off your shoulders. Joke around with your partner, your kids, yourself. Call good friends for a chat and some silliness. Let your heart be light, and look on the bright side of difficult situations.

5. **Try not to burden your partner with grim realities,** at least not on the emotional level. If you can translate these into specific needs okay, but otherwise forget it. Take responsibility for your feelings. Find other women to talk to for solace and inspiration.

6. **Know that this wild and crazy time will pass.** Keep the long-term view in mind, plan your first weekend (or week-long) getaway with pleasure, and keep the faith.

Finally, it's important to note that against all the odds, a fair number of women feel their sexual understanding and power greatly enhanced by giving birth. Some have orgasms for the first time in their lives. This is probably because birth partners a woman primarily with herself; the particulars of letting go and surrendering come ultimately from within her. Especially if she has been buffeted around by male needs, desires and opinions about sex, this can come as quite a revelation.

As Cassie says: 'I never had orgasms like I did after giving birth. When I was pushing my daughter out, I got more than connected to my vaginal muscles. I *became* them. My strength was incredible, my timing exquisite. Before, when I made love it was me up here, vagina down there. But now my consciousness and intelligence are fully inside me. I'm not afraid to do or try anything with my vagina; its power belongs to me. Once you've let go giving birth, letting go with sex can take you to places you've never dreamed of.'

1. Newton, Niles and Modahl, Charlotte, 'Mood State Differences Between Breast and Bottle-Feeding Mothers', *Newton on Breastfeeding* (Seattle, Birth & Life Bookstore, 1990)
2. Thoman, E.B., Wetzel, A., Levine, S., 'Lactation Prevents Disruption of Temperature Regulation and Suppresses Adrenocortical Activity in Rats', *Communicative Behavior in Biology* (Vol. 2, Part A, 1968)
3. Newton, Niles, 'The Role of the Oxytocin Reflexes in Three Interpersonal Reproductive Acts: Coitus, Birth and Breastfeeding', *Newton on Breastfeeding* (Seattle, Birth & Life Bookstore, 1990)
4. Steinem, Gloria, *Revolution From Within* (Boston, Little, Brown, 1992)
5. Masters, W.H., Johnson, V.E., *Human Sexual Response* (Boston, Little, Brown, 1966)

# 5

# Sex and the superwoman (or supermum)

You are a woman of the 1990s: in a word, busy. You juggle, often frantically, the demands of work, family and personal relationships. If you have a male partner, you may still do the majority of the housework, run the errands, pay the bills, buy the clothing, supervise household repairs, cook, wash the clothes. You are likely to be the primary go-between with your children's teachers, making time for parents' evenings and help with homework. Once in a great while, you might find time to have lunch with a friend. And perhaps you plan birthday parties, holidays, buy presents, write thank-you letters and notes of acknowledgement. If you also happen to run your own business, you are definitely in deep water!

The fact is, it's no longer a matter of choice for most women to work outside the home. Our economy has become inflated to the point that two incomes per family are almost essential. Meanwhile, the desperate need for daily renewal is brushed aside for greater productivity.

Who has time, really, for a regular ritual of self-care? We're lucky to get out of the house on time, or find a moment's rest before going to bed. What's more, as we begin to age and must face new challenges to health and well-being, society continues to perpetuate youth culture via a barrage of skin-care lines, fitness aids, and so on. Many women feel they barely get by day to day, let alone have time to make any effort to turn back the clock.

Is there no way out of this dilemma? Before we can realistically discuss the impact of the superwoman syndrome on sexuality, we must realise just how incompatible the two are. In so many varied and complex ways, lack of time to care for oneself greatly diminishes sexual desire.

Yes, there are decent stop-gap measures, such as the weekend getaway, luncheon rendezvous or private evening out. These do help to maintain a sense of balance by providing escape and relief from tension. But ultimately, snatched moments together are not enough because real intimacy cannot be staged or forced; it must be based on genuine communication. If communication is continually disrupted or shelved indefinitely, sudden episodes of private time can end up in arguments, or long, involved discussions that sap instead of renew. As Margaret reports, 'We'd start out with a romantic meal or something, then wild and crazy sex. But when we finally got down to talking, I felt this resentment ... why do I have to do it all? The day-to-day routine is bad enough, but even on vacation, I'm initiating talks and fielding the upsets. I feel unseen, invisible. I'm taking care of everything and everybody, but nobody cares for me.'

## TRANSFORMING SEX-ROLE EXPECTATIONS

Margaret's lament hits it right on the mark for many of us. Unfortunately, the solution isn't any easier to bear than the problem but here it is: the only one who can really take care of Margaret is Margaret herself. This means revamping priorities so that her own are at the top. Further, her entire sex-role image must be reconditioned from serving others to nurturing herself. This is a drastic shift from what our mothers believed and what society continues to expect of us.

This is especially difficult in that society also refuses to accord women equal rights and privileges to those held by men. As a group, men have a higher pay scale, greater social security benefits, more free time and more opportunity to play. With our role as servant so deeply entrenched in social structure, in the institutions of marriage, education, healthcare, business and religion, we are going to have to assert loud and clear just exactly what we need, and how and when we need it. To quote once again the indomitable Camille Paglia, 'Feminism begins at home. It begins with every single woman drawing the line.'[1] At first, this seems like yet another job to do. But this is the task that can cause inappropriate or demeaning roles to fall by the wayside; this is the key to revolution. If men, women and children are not equals in their fundamental rights then our world will be out of balance, plagued with war, famine, disease and poverty. That such is indeed the case makes the need for our assertion more than a personal matter; it is politically, socially and ecologically imperative.

For years, women were taught to be peacemakers, to soothe and heal, to handle the emotional problems of others. When we behave thus, it's no wonder that we find men to be out of touch with their feelings. It is true that men have an inherent difficulty, due to brain structure and function, in linking emotion to other aspects of behaviour and response. But why should we go so far as to translate their emotions for them? Perhaps we would find less resentment on their part if we focused our efforts on putting *our* feelings, needs and desires forward overtly, rather than covertly. This is a very different model of relationship than the norm, but might serve to create a healthier sort of intimacy.

One woman shared with me these words from her husband: 'You know, you women think you have it so hard, but at least you know what you're fighting for. You've got principles ... for us guys, if we start to open up and change, it's pretty confusing.' Although we may feel compassion for men in this quandary, we must continuously beware of rescuing them. When we do, we perpetuate the problem by collusion.

Much has been said of late about women's anger, but what about that of men? Ours is fairly easy to root in inequality, overwork and unsupportive social structures; in general, we are angry at society. For men, it is different; society is basically supportive and is therefore not the target, but women are. Rape is an obvious sign of this and violent pornography further serves to illustrate the problem. Men are angry at women for brushing them off, abandoning them to their own confusion, failing to make the pain and frustration of life easier to bear. And it's true – many women are just too busy to bother with male angst as they once did.

On the other hand, the stress of competing in a man's world has led some women to adopt male characteristics almost to the exclusion of their own. So deeply have women rebelled against being stereotyped as weak, indecisive and irrational that they have likewise rejected the positive side of these aspects: vulnerability, flexibility and creativity. True, women have practically been forced to do so in order to move up the ladder of success. But perhaps it is time to expand a bit, and reincorporate the more feminine aspects of our personalities into our way of life, our approach to problem solving and our relationships.

In *Men, Women and Relationships*, Gray describes four core male-female personality configurations. Of particular interest here is the woman so independent that she has severed critical ties with others and herself. We know her by the following: 1) she is overly defensive; 2) she is compulsively organised and overly responsible; 3) she is suspicious, cold and critical; 4) she is pushy and manipulative; 5) she is tense, intolerant, judgemental and impatient; 6) she is unable to accept support. Again, it is easy to see how many of the brightest and most creative women of our time have wound up in this condition. But this is clearly an imbalanced way of being, a state at odds with health and happiness, sexual receptivity and pleasure.[2]

As Stacy relates, 'I kept blaming Bob, but I knew it was me. I had become so sharp with him, so on-edge all the time, so critical and controlling that we just didn't get along. I convinced myself that sex was still fine; after all, I knew well enough to let my guard down in bed. But the chemistry between us the rest of the time, the erotic side of our day-to-day contact was missing.'

For the most part, women need intimate relationships in their lives to reflect back meaning and significance. Women are so expansive by nature that, as a matter of course, their energies become overly diffused. Their intimate connections help them reconnect with themselves. This ties in with women's tendency to consolidate their understanding of a matter by talking it through with close friends, formulating and evolving their thoughts aloud. In *Women's Ways of Knowing*, this unique ability of women to share half-formed truths (in contrast to the male preference for holding forth with already polished positions) was referred to by women themselves as 'real talk'.[3]

To further complicate matters, some men have sought to subdue their masculine traits and have overemphasised the feminine. Although it's generally good for men to be open, sensitive and easy-going, some go overboard and become overwhelmed, confused, indecisive and irresponsible on a somewhat permanent basis. Particularly when a man begins to live on dreams or becomes moody and withdrawn much of the time, it is clear that something is wrong.

In either extreme, sex will definitely be affected because the fundamental charge and attraction between opposites has been severely altered. The irony is that we tend to subvert our sexual happiness in relationships by trying to make our partners more manageable, more predictable and more like ourselves. But as our differences diminish, so will the attraction. We turn into good friends instead of lovers; the passion is gone. 'To whatever extent a partner must suppress their ways of being, feeling, thinking or doing in order to receive love or be safe in a relationship, the passion will fade.'[4]

This does indeed raise complex issues, and there is no easy way to turn things around. But in general, women can benefit simply by recognising their feminine and masculine traits and keeping an eye on the balance. Changes in lifestyle, rhythms of activity and rest may be in order. Today's woman needs to find particular practices that evoke the feminine, whatever they may be. Sometimes, the only way she can discover these is by breaking her routine, perhaps by taking a holiday. Dialling and tuning the male and female in yourself can be fun. To be able to do so is a landmark of maturity and it is bound to have an enriching effect on your sexuality.

Speaking of maturity, a woman's age or stage of life will also have an effect on all this. Taking the broad view, it makes sense that the tremendous push for security and success during our twenties and thirties might lead to a values and identity crisis in our forties. And it should come as no surprise that a similar crisis might follow sexually. For a woman, sex in young adulthood is largely about identifying with and pleasing another. Sex in the thirties tends to focus on pair-bonding and/or procreation. And sex in mid-life establishes the priorities of the self: physical, emotional and spiritual. Often, when we think of sexual changes in mid-life we think of the stereotypical male response of having affairs with other women. More on this later, but for now, listen to Barbara's story:

> My husband had affairs from the time he turned 40, and I only found out three years later. I was so furious, so humiliated that I really didn't think we were going to make it. Couldn't sleep with him at all, but he wanted to stay so we had counselling. All that stuff, I'll spare you – but when we finally started making love again, I was a different women. I went out for myself. Whenever the pain of his betrayal would start to get to me, I'd hold on to myself and just do what I felt was best for me. I got in touch with a strength I didn't know I had before, and I aligned myself with it, even in bed.

Of course, there are many women who choose with all good reason to cut their losses on pain like this and move on. Other women have affairs of their own, in search of healing. The point is that what Barbara called aligning with herself, her strength, becomes more and more critical to women as they mature. Ultimately, it paves the way for menopause and old-age, when nerve and gumption enable us to weather challenges to our health and mobility.

Here's an interesting comment from a friend several weeks after her fortieth birthday: 'I thought mid-life crises were only for men. But it's really hit me. I'm turning into a real loud mouth, saying things to my boss and husband I wouldn't have *dreamed* of saying before! You figure you have only so much time ... I feel almost ruthless about getting my needs met.'

And what was this doing to her sex life? 'This is pretty personal, but in the middle of making love one night I just blurted out, "Joe, why don't you *concentrate*?" I never said anything like that before ... see, my husband just tends to ramble on sometimes in bed, without focusing on me. When he paused (I guess he was a little shocked), I added, "You know, concentrate on me." I couldn't believe I did that!'

Often, a revamping of role expectations results in a shock to intimacy phase. The love and friendliness are still there, but the old sexual patterns just don't fit. A couple may find themselves taking a sexual break, and worrying about it all the way (more on this in Chapter Eight). Says Susan, 'When I started to be truthful with my partner, I was pretty scared. Scared he wouldn't love me, wouldn't care, or even worse, *couldn't* help me. We were both surprised, I think, to find that we kept on going and things began to change. But for a while, we couldn't make love. A lot was being stirred up for both of us.'

How to respond to estrangement depends largely on what is causing it, on the underlying issues. Sometimes a couple can handle these on their own; other times, extra support and counselling become necessary. And it may be that patience with one another, via an agreement to 'give it some time,' will allow for spontaneous resolution.

## SEX AND ANGER

On the other hand, if there is deep-seated anger, sexual
intimacy may all but vanish. As expert Marilyn Ruman,
Ph.D., says, 'Anger is almost always the enemy of desire
and is one of the best places to look when your sex life if
floundering.'[5]

Often, couples are not fully aware of how angry they are.
In the classic passive-aggressive mode, a woman may force
her partner to act out her frustrations by her own continual
resistance and avoidance. Her partner, of course, may do
likewise. This sort of pattern generally has roots in a
childhood with parents who enacted extremes of submission and domination. Particularly in situations involving
chemical dependency and/or abuse, the survivor frequently
comes to believe that expressing anger in relationship leads
only to unhappiness.

The shadow side of anger is sadness and loss. Generally,
the longer a couple has been together, the more each
expects the other to be able to make this loss up to them.
Unfortunately, this seldom takes place on a conscious
level.

One way to get at the work of healing is to recognise that
anger correlates to need. It is important to express anger,
yes, but even more critical to articulate the need it
represents. If a couple can agree to acknowledge one
another's needs, and meet them whenever possible, intimacy may soon resurface.

It may also be necessary to weed out patterns of
avoidance in the relationship. Spending inordinate
amounts of time in separate parts of the house, taking
meals separately, going to bed at different times or arguing

just before bed are classic examples. Not taking care of oneself physically, neglecting shared environments (particularly the bedroom) or cluttering free time with small talk and housework are other clues. Making changes in these areas, as well as expressing needs to one another regularly (perhaps on a daily basis at first), will get the relationship back on track. If certain patterns of avoidance seem deeply entrenched, it may be wise to see a counsellor.

## STRESS AND SEXUALITY

Let's backtrack a bit, and examine more fully the effects of stress on sexuality. To do so, we must consider the physical effects of stress on the adrenal glands. The adrenals are comprised of two parts, the medulla and the cortex. Under stress, the medulla produces catecholamines, one of which is adrenaline, responsible for the flight or fight response we feel when threatened or under fire. The cortex, on the other hand, produces the sex hormones oestrogen and progesterone, but more significantly, the androgens responsible for the libido (sex drive). To some degree these functions are opposing; if for example, stress is chronic or protracted so that the medulla must continually pump the body with catecholamines, the production of androgens from the cortex may be neglected. Here we have a physiological explanation of how stress may dampen sexual desire.

Psychologically, stress causes us to withdraw in order to consolidate ourselves, to hold back from sharing with another. Sexual activity under these circumstances simply may not occur, or if it does, it may be brief and fairly explosive (nothing wrong with that, but it doesn't do much on the emotional level, particularly if both partners are under stress). The challenges of unwinding in bed, encountering emotions carefully held in check, or stumbling on outright blocks while trying to coordinate with another person struggling with the same process can be formidable enough to dissuade one from even making the effort. And some couples do fine with non-sexual phases if they keep the communication going in other ways, particularly through shared activities that both enjoy.

Others choose to just have sex, be it good, bad or indifferent, for the sake of keeping a sense of connection and physical closeness. From Natalie: 'It's rough for us right now: we both knock ourselves out at work, the kids get little of our attention, we both feel guilty and angry, and often we take it out on each other. Then we have sex to make up. Sometimes it's great, a real release. Sometimes it just doesn't make it; we're still all bottled up, and we feel more separate than before. But that's marriage, I guess.'

Either way, couples suffering from chronic stress will find it an obstacle to intimacy. And the answer lies not in the bedroom, but in learning to recognise the problem and handle it intelligently. To complicate matters, men and women generally have different reactions to stress. Whereas men tend to pull back and withdraw to consider the situation objectively, women often respond with a rush of emotion; they need to sift through their feelings and discuss them with someone in order to find stability. This is how women separate their needs from the needs of others, and avoid becoming overwhelmed.

Women who are overwhelmed have one particular characteristic in common: they lose the ability to prior-itise.[6] Every task and obligation suddenly assumes equal importance. Whether it's finishing up a project to meet a deadline or folding the laundry, everything is done in a continuous overwrought stream of activity, rather like a runaway train.

When a woman gets more and more removed from her

feelings, she is likely to overreact to the inconsequential. Not being conscious of important issues, she will find little irritations and focus her frustration and anger on these. Every woman knows the idiotic feeling of exploding in anger over the unwashed dishes, or the single paper napkin scuttling about the floor. From this point on, total exhaustion is forthcoming. We feel utterly drained, sapped of our strength, useless and depressed. This scenario takes its toll on everyone involved; when we hit bottom, we see clearly that the long-suffering, self-negating approach to stress and its causes does not work.

If stress is due to illness or a crisis involving a loved one or family member, outside support becomes crucial. Even if the situation cannot be altered, at least it can be tempered with understanding and made somewhat tolerable. Again, the media has misled us by overly portraying the happy family, particularly on TV; seldom do we see serious crises without immediate resolution, or the protracted stress and agony of losing an intimate friend to terminal illness, addiction or other destructive behaviour (more on this in Chapter Eight). Maintaining personal autonomy is the key, for it is the only way to be renewed and thus strong enough to care for another. Beyond support, we need outside activities, structure and routine, and meaningful work to do. Sex may be low on the list of priorities, but it can serve to renew and strengthen us if we but recognise the range of emotions we bring to it.

## HOW CHILDREN AFFECT SEXUALITY

Let's look specifically at how having children may affect our sexuality. We'll consider some of the key developmental phases in children's lives, and how these might affect the inclination for and enjoyment of sex.

T. Berry Brazelton, authority on child rearing and development, notes that as a child reaches the age of two, parents may begin to compete for his or her affections.[7] If competition and/or poor communication exist in other areas of their lives (which is probable, considering how little time parents of a toddler have for themselves and each other), they may become estranged and dysfunctional as a unit. In other words, for want of privacy and intimacy with one another, parents may transfer their needs onto their child and begin to vie bitterly for his or her attention.

If this situation is neglected, studies show that the time most likely for new parents to engage in extramarital affairs is when the child is three or four. By then, the sheer survival issues of the first few years have been surmounted and parents have an opportunity to view the wreckage. Along the way, the tensions of sleep deprivation, continuous interruption and other stresses have called for relief, but all too often, parents vent their anger and frustration in private, or may take it out on each other. Thus it may be that by baby's fourth birthday, parents view each other as less than friends, and sex with an outsider not such a far-fetched idea.

There are things you can do to forestall such a crisis. Here are some suggestions:

### Take Private Time

This is *not* optional! It is the first principle in finding the energy and enthusiasm for relating to another. One way to do this is to squeeze time out of your usual routine. For example, time-saving devices like slow cookers and rice cookers or pre-washed salad greens can simplify meals so much that you have an extra hour free before dinner. Or you can arrange chores to run simultaneously instead of

one-by-one, saving time and steps. Changing your standards of order and cleanliness with regard to the house may
also save time and your nerves.

Another more lasting and self-affirming approach is to
change the usual routine so that time for yourself is a
natural part of it. Teach your children, right from the start,
how to take care of themselves. Many of us were brought
up by post-war parents who wanted to give us the best of
everything, and in truth, they overdid it. We need to create
a healthier model whereby every family member does his or
her share. This may also mean teaching your husband to
take care of himself, as well as performing his rightful share
of household duties. If you are in a position to hire help, *do
it*. Save your marriage by keeping hold of yourself.

Housework is such a charged issue for most couples that
it deserves a few more words. With regard to marriage and
sticking together, author Andrew Ward dryly advises, 'It
doesn't matter if one of you spends all day on the patio
eating bonbons, you've got to divide housework right
down the middle. Actual equalised work schedules, imper-
vious to the shirker and martyr among you (shirkers and
martyrs compose most married couples), should be ham-
mered out right away and signed, preferably in blood, by
both parties.'[8]

### Keep Up With Your Dreams

Don't let them get away, or fade so you no longer recognise
them. Take them to review your goals in life and fantasies
of what could be, giving yourself free rein to be visionary.
Where do you want to be a year from now, five, ten? What
are the things you feel you absolutely must do in life or you
won't really have lived? Some say that whatever you loved
to do when you were seven or eight years old holds the key

to your future. Think back, dream forward, and keep track.

### Make Time For The Relationship

When you are very busy, intimacy must be made a priority if you expect to enjoy it day to day. This means setting aside 'couple-time' – literally scheduling it in. Maintain a regular date night. And set aside another time, preferably in the morning when you are both fresh, to talk together about what is going on in your lives and how you feel about it. This is a time for open sharing and disclosure, with ground rules of hearing one another out without being judgemental. Some couples do this daily, others once a week but the more you do it, the more it will tend to occur spontaneously.

Never underestimate the power of an entire night alone together. There is a big difference between sex when you know you might be awakened or interrupted, and sex with both total privacy and the freedom to get into it again a little later. Perhaps you have forgotten this, but take my word for it! At least twice a year, you must get away to some romantic and enjoyable location and recreate your love.

### Surprise Yourself and Your Lover

In a nutshell, do the unexpected once in a while. When you were courting, a lot of excitement was generated by doing new things together, sharing adventures, discovering mutual reactions to foreign situations. Let this element of excitement back into your life, and don't worry too much about appearing foolish. Take a few risks and try new things, food, clothing, kinds of entertainment and places to go. Often we marry because we have tired of running around with little or no stability in our lives; we long for a nice simple routine. But routine is routine, it needs the spice of innovation to keep it from becoming dull. Taking in new impressions is a time-honoured way of stimulating creativity and passion. Reanimate!

### Get Help If You Need It

Marriage/couple counselling doesn't have to be a long-term proposition. People often end up in counselling because it is the only way they seem able to make the time to talk to one another. As long as there are no serious problems in the marriage such as abuse or violence, counselling can be a simple matter of letting someone more objective observe your process of communication and help you be more personally effective and mutually receptive to one another. From there, new patterns of behaviour can be created so that you can discern and solve problems on your own. Almost every intimate partnership needs a boost like this once in a while.

Another critical time for mothers is when their child begins school full-time, or is secondary school age. Clearly, the child is no longer an infant, and all the trappings of that phase come to an end. Between the ages of five and seven, children identify with the family unit; thereafter, they begin to identify with society at large. If a mother has been at home full-time, she will be called upon to change her relationship with her child. Or if she's been unable to spend much time with her child, she may feel great loss and longing for the irreplaceable phase she's missed. These emotions may be difficult to share with one's partner because they so strongly characterise the mother–infant bond, though increasingly, men who have provided lots of care in the early years understand and feel them too. If not, men tend to dismiss these blues as the height of irrationality. They remember the sleepless nights, the teething, the mad shuffle for babysitters, the interrupted lovemaking, and above all, their partner's complaints, and wonder how she can possibly be serious!

What it really comes down to is reassembling your identity and establishing new goals for yourself and the relationship. Especially for the full-time mum with time on her hands, the questions are tough: what do I do now? Who am I, with my child out of my arms and off to school? Now is the time when recalling your ambitions becomes crucial. Particularly if a woman has given up her career for motherhood and is thinking of going back to it, she must take a hard look at just how far she has fallen behind.

In any period of change, we cling to the past to find courage for the future. We use what we have been as a springboard for what we will become. Listen to what Christine had to say at this juncture: 'I was happy Zoe was off to school, but I did feel empty a little, too. Especially with my husband, Jon – I just couldn't make him understand. Really, I didn't understand it myself, until one day it was suddenly clear. Before, when I was recovering from the birth and trying to get my body back, I wanted him to love me for what I was before – to remind me, you know? Now, with Zoe out in the world, I want him to reaffirm me as her mother, love me for that. That I don't *have* to be anything else.'

Here again we have an example of a woman wanting reassurance from her partner that she really needs to give herself. The important thing is to see in these feelings the seeds of growth and change, and then respond accordingly.

Another challenging phase for a mother is the onset of

adolescence, particularly with a daughter. I recall describing mine at age 11 as being in a perpetual state of PMS. This is also the time when girls typically find fault with their mothers, particularly in the area of personal appearance. I remember coming out dressed for a party one night when my daughter remarked quite caustically, 'You're not going to wear *that*, are you?' The stress of the situation is compounded if mum has reached some major chronological landmark of her own, say, her fortieth birthday. In spite of herself, she may end up making expensive trips to the cosmetics counter, beauty salon, or slimmers' group. Not necessarily bad, all this, but the upshot may be marked and persistent uncertainty about her physical attributes and basic sex appeal.

This is further complicated by the natural shift in power that occurs in adolescence. Particularly if your style has been strictly to enforce your will on your young ones, their natural rebellion at this age can leave you feeling utterly powerless. And in truth, the role of parent does begin to change from guardian to guide and confidant. As the bread-baking theory of child rearing goes, you mix and add ingredients when children are young, you watch the dough rise (and must deflate it occasionally) as they mature, but once in the oven of adolescence, you'd better not open the door! Yes, you keep an eye on things, but you don't interfere unless the bread is about to burn. If, however, a woman is herself in upheaval with mid-life reassessment, she is likely to struggle with this shift more than usual and take it as yet another blow to her already fragile self-confidence. This may merit a call to a counsellor or support network of some kind.

## THE MID-LIFE TURNAROUND

Women's concerns about their attractiveness as they approach the age of forty are bound to arise, whether they have a teenage daughter or not. Entire industries are built on the expectation that women will consume almost anything to stay young. Anti-ageing creams, plastic surgery, hair colouring, liposuction: the list is endless. Most women seem to accept the inevitability of aging by their mid-forties, but many spend the latter part of their thirties experimenting heavily to see what, if anything, they can forestall. This is also prime time for putting on airs in the bedroom that are less than convincing to either party. Joan remarked, 'Really, I was obsessed with my appearance, my fears of getting older, or that Fred would find someone else. I started dressing up (or down) for him more, wearing the sexiest stuff I could find. But it didn't work, he just seemed ill at ease. Later, he said he felt pressured by me when he just wanted to relax and enjoy having sex.'

Sometime in their forties, women usually come to terms with advancing age by finding an exercise programme, beauty regimen and other lifestyle modifications to suit their needs. Not that anxiety about ageing won't rear its head from time to time, but as women advance through this decade the business of consolidating themselves, their work and relationships, takes precedence. 'Forty and fabulous': you know what works for you, you speak your mind, your strategies are tried and true, you have a solid base from which to innovate, and success may be yours for the taking!

It is a well-known fact that whereas men reach their sexual peak (as per intensity and endurance) in their early twenties, women reach theirs later, often in their forties. This is partly physical, partly psychological. For many women, it takes that long to get to know themselves sexually, to overcome taboos of sexual self-expression, to come to know and trust their bodies, and to be confident enough to let go and get what they want in bed.

This is also a time when women who have never fantasised before find their sexual imaginations coming to life. In her book, *Women On Top*, author Nancy Friday makes clear both the range and outrageousness of women's sexual fantasies as they reach this peak. Interestingly, these fantasies are quite physically oriented, focused on ways of maximising sensation, while the fantasies of younger women are more emotionally based. For example, the woman in her twenties might fantasise about a romantic build-up and tender preludes to intercourse, whereas the mid-life woman focuses more on positions, techniques of her partner, or even on bondage and multiple partners as enhancements to her sensation.

June Reinisch, in the Kinsey Report, notes that men and women do a turnaround in sexual temperament about this time. As women become more physically orientated and intrigued with physical experimentation, men become interested in letting themselves be vulnerable and caring.[9] These changes are, in fact, hormonally based, for as women reach menopause and their oestrogen level decreases, testosterone decreases in men. Women become more masculine; men, more feminine. This explains a little under-stood fact about men in mid-life crises; they tend to seek out younger women not so much for the wild re-enactment of youthful passion, but because these women are sexually oriented precisely as they themselves wish to be: emotion-ally and romantically. Yes, this strikes women in their forties as the height of irony: all those years they yearned for romance, while he wanted nothing but sex! It appears that nature designed the sexes to be persistently at odds and thus complementary (although they do become more alike in later years). The trick is to turn these facts of life to one's advantage (which some women do by forming liaisons with younger men).

Polarisation occurs when give and take turns into take and take, which is all the more likely to happen in the mid-life crunch of overwork and overextension. Says Laurie, 'At first, I thought there was something wrong with my partner, that he was slowing down, losing his grip for some physical reason. This happened about the same time I seemed to want sex to be more physically forceful than before: faster, rougher. I found myself getting impatient with Ken, wishing he'd get on with it, at the same time feeling like a heel for being so pushy and demanding. But damn, what I wanted felt right to me, and I didn't want to put on the brakes.'

This is a good start; the feeling is genuine and it fits with the natural shift. But there will be a breakdown here without frank communication, understanding and mutual support. If he wants to take more time warming up, choose your favourite foreplay and spell it out, loud and clear. If he's pacing himself to the utmost, initiate changes in position that keep the stimulation level high enough for you. Bring your fantasies into the picture somehow. And don't be surprised if he is the one wanting afterglow cuddling and pillow talk!

The positive side of these changes is illustrated by these words from Candace: 'We'd been together for 12 years, and I finally felt like our sex life was really on track. We truly understood where the other was coming from, because we'd each pretty much been there ourselves – we'd run the gamut, I guess! Sex just got better and better, and we had an ongoing sexual dimension in our communication that I remembered from the early stages of our relationship. It surprised me, exceeded my expectations and was well worth waiting for.'

This may also be a point when women seek relationships with other women for the first time, finding both personal and worldly egalitarianism. As Lynn reports, 'I never considered myself bisexual, never thought of being with a woman until I reached a place of certainty and confidence in myself that made me long for the affinity of an equal. I'd been with so many men, struggling with their problems. Then I fell in love with Susan, and found common life experience, humour, flexibility and passion perfect for this time of my life.'

In the next chapter, we will look at the effects of meno-pause on sexuality, as well as sex in later years. With the help of some fascinating cross-cultural research, we will hopefully lay to rest any notions that older women aren't particularly interested in sex.

1. Paglia, Camille, 'Hurricane Camille Wreaks Havoc', *San Francisco Chronicle* (September 1992)
2. Gray, John, *Men, Women and Relationships* (Hillsboro, Oregon, Beyond Words Publishing, 1990)
3. Belenky, M.F., Clinchy, B.M., Goldberg, N.R., Tarule, J.M., *Women's Ways of Knowing* (New York, Basic Books, 1986)
4. *ibid.*
5. Ruman, Marilyn, *New Woman* (April, 1991)
6. Gray, *Men, Women and Relationships*
7. Brazelton, T. Berry, *Infants and Mothers* (New York, Delacorte Press, 1969)
8. Ward, Andrew, *Out Here* (New York, Penguin Books, 1991)
9. Reinisch, June, 'The Kinsey Report' (syndicated) *San Francisco Chronicle* (1990)

# 6

# The menopause and sex in later years

The menopause – I doubt we could find a word more fraught with negative connotations for women. But it's not just the inevitability of old age signalled by the menopause that causes distress, it's the process itself, with its tempestuous and uncontrollable physical and emotional side effects. Who has time for all that, in the midst of family obligations and a career most likely at its peak? How are we to cope, for example, with the disruption and embarrassment of hot flushes in the middle of an important presentation or social occasion? And how do we handle the distress of vaginal dryness when we really want to make love?

Add to these difficulties an array of cultural bias against ageing, particularly for women, who often find themselves bereft of identity as they grow older, and it's no wonder we approach the menopause with a sense of dread. But there are other ways to view the process that accord women greater dignity and self-respect, so that the benefits of this phase, not the least of which are sexual, may be readily recognised and enjoyed.

## WHAT IS THE MENOPAUSE?

Beyond the obvious cessation of menstruation are the underlying causes. At puberty, a girl has approximately 300,000 follicles, or egg forming cells, whereas a woman approaching the menopause has only 8,000 or so remaining. The eggs are destroyed by a combination of stress, radiation (via sun exposure), or natural degeneration according to built-in lifespan. As the eggs diminish in number, ovulation may not occur. And unless an egg ripens, there will be no corpus luteum to release progesterone. Despite the fact that the pituitary tries to compensate with extra surges of FSH and LH, the ovaries become less and less responsive and their production of oestrogen eventually ceases.

The menopause occurs on average between the ages of 48 and 52 but some women stop menstruating as early as their late thirties. And before the periods actually cease there are four to six years when hormone levels progressively decline. Thus the menopause may be divided into two phases: premenopausal and menopausal. The premenopause is characterised by sharp fluctuations in levels of progesterone (oestrogen diminishes steadily, whereas if no egg ripens in a particular cycle, progesterone will drop abruptly). This leads to sporadic bleeding, changes in cycle length and amount of bleeding with menstruation. Commonly, periods come closer together and become much heavier; bleeding for a week to ten days is not unusual. Problems can occur if blood loss is extreme, if bleeding lasts further into the cycle or if cumulative blood loss becomes excessive.

Sometimes a D and C is done in these cases, and cells from the uterus are checked for any sign of abnormality. Cancer, polyps and fibroid growths are possible causes, and can thus be ruled out. But most of the time, the problem is simply that progesterone levels are not adequate to maintain the uterine lining. Changes in diet and lifestyle, along with herbal remedies, may be of benefit. Studies have shown that deficiencies of iron, vitamin C and bioflavonoids can exacerbate heavy bleeding. Cigarette smoking, stress and excessive intake of alcohol can also contribute to the problem.

Some women have little trouble with progesterone-related symptoms and notice only that their periods are coming less often and are becoming lighter. This is when the well-known symptoms of the menopause – the hot flushes, mood swings, night sweats and vaginal changes – come into play. About 80 per cent of women experience some of these symptoms while passing through the menopause.

When a woman has stopped menstruating for a full year the menopause is considered to be complete. The age at which the menopause occurs is somewhat hereditary; if a woman's mother or sisters were early or late, she is likely to follow suit. For whatever reason, women in industrialised countries are experiencing menarche earlier than in the past, and the menopause later and later. The average age is now 51; at the turn of the century it was 46. Considering that in those days, life expectancy was little more than 50 years, it is easy to see the foundation of persisting beliefs that the menopause marks the beginning of the end. But today's woman can expect to live to the age of 78, thus finishing the menopause with nearly a third of her life still ahead.

What will this last third of her life be like? Is she doomed, as the media would generally have us believe, to be shrivelled and sexless – a doddery 'senior citizen'? That depends largely on how well she takes care of herself, and how she defines herself socially and individually. But first, she must find a way to make it through 'the change'.

Male authorities on the subject have been little more than harbingers of doom. Robert A. Wilson, author of *Feminine Forever*, and staunch advocate of hormone replacement therapy (HRT), describes the menopause as 'the loss of womanhood and the loss of good health', claiming that chemical imbalance results in 'castration' and a state of 'living decay'.[1] David Reuben, author of *Everything You Always Wanted to Know About Sex but Were Afraid to Ask*, summarily expresses the antiquated view of the menopause as the end point for women: 'Having outlived their ovaries, they may have outlived their usefulness as human beings. The remaining years may just be marking time until they follow their glands into oblivion.'[2] Sheila Kitzinger, on the other hand, sees menopausal changes as those by which 'a new balance is found, one which is natural and right for an older woman', through a process she likens to adolescence.[3] She is quick to point out that although oestrogen and progesterone diminish greatly, they continue to be produced postmenopause by the hormone testosterone. Susan Lark, author of *The Menopause Self-Help Book*, notes that many women pay better attention to their diet and lifestyle during the menopause, so that these years become exciting and enriching, a time of 'vigor and vitality'.

The key, I think, is to view the menopause as a natural transition, but a transition nonetheless. In other words, it is a period of intense and incontrovertible change, marked by extremes. And, as is true of the transition phase of childbirth or the premenstrual phase of the monthly cycle, success is found not in trying to take charge or get control of the situation but by cooperating with it, seeing it through. Premenstrually or in labour, there are specific coping techniques for dealing with physical and emotional difficulties; the same is true in the menopause. But beyond all this, trust in the process as natural, positive and non-threatening will be the determining factor in the ease of its progression, the triumph in its completion and the insight gleaned along the way.

Our culture places so great a premium on feminine constancy that women are often denied the right to experience the heights and depths of life, as men do by acts of daring and bravado, creativity and delusion, rebellion and peace. For women, the ability to know these things is there in the flesh, patterned hormonally in a sequence that repeatedly comes full circle and gives meaning and continuity to life. But certain phases are undeniably tumultuous and extreme.

Characteristic of any period of transition is the chance to take stock, to assess where we've been and where we have yet to go. Typical mid-life comments like, 'I haven't accomplished what I hoped in my career', or, 'I feel unfulfilled in my primary relationships', hold keys for formulating new plans. Sweeping changes can, and probably should, occur at this time. A third of one's life yet to be lived is quite a long time, especially with the benefit of experience. It would be foolish not to use this transition for a few radical departures and explorations into the unknown.

And, in this regard, it is probable that anything we cling to which needs to be released will tend to make the menopause worse. Women now have lives outside the home, and for the most part, are having children later than ever before. Surely it is not easy to go through the menopause when your children are struggling with adolescence, but it must be even harder if they have recently left home and you are utterly at a loss for what to do. In reading first-person accounts from both past and present menopausal women, the main thing they share is an emphasis on letting go, carrying on, finding new work to do, new ways to get more out of life.

There is no direct correlation between premenstrual and menopausal difficulties, yet the process of handling them is much the same. A certain percentage of our premenstrual outbursts are highly irrational, and of little consequence. But the intensity of our outbursts reveals our tension level, how much we're holding in or holding back. Winding up, or winding down from such an explosion, we may glimpse the underlying meaning or the cause of what we feel, along with some intimation of what to do about it. It seems clear that decreased oestrogen and increased testosterone coincide with menopausal women's need for self-assertion.

## PHYSICAL SYMPTOMS AND TREATMENT

Many symptoms of the menopause are autonomic, such as hot flushes, sweating, heart palpitations, and itching of the skin. Others are physical or metabolic, such as vaginal dryness, bladder dysfunction, bone thinning (osteoporosis), joint pain, muscular weakness, shrinking and sagging of the breasts, skin drying and wrinkling, thinning of the hair, weight gain, or periodic complaints of bloating and headache. Emotional symptoms include moodiness, irritability, depression, insomnia, forgetfulness, and changes in sexual function or desire. Approaches to dealing with these symptoms fall basically into two camps: one, of obliteration through hormonal control; two, of cooperation by way of health-enhancing natural practices and methods of response.

Hormonal replacement treatment was the brainchild of physicians (such as the aforementioned Wilson) who perceived the menopause, along with childbearing and menstruation, as little more than diseases requiring medication. An interesting aside that serves as an illustration: one of my students recounted how her mother, in giving birth to her, had called the doctor a 'goddam son-of-a-bitch' at the height of transition, and was promptly sedated. Let's face it: most men feel more than a little threatened in the midst of biological transitions, particularly when at full throttle, and have long sought ways to dominate and control women at these junctures. Medication is a powerful way to do this. This is not to discount the value of and need for hormonal replacement in certain circumstances, but the routine use of hormones to address common complaints of the menopause is just as bad as drugging the body in childbirth, or obliterating premenstrual symptoms with sedatives. HRT was, in fact, touted as the only way menopausal women might hope to stay youthful; in the 1960s, it was considered a panacea for sleeplessness, depression, loss of interest in sex, dry skin and hair, fatigue – in other words, all the undesired effects of ageing.

Although oestrogen replacement can have a positive effect on hot flushes, vaginal changes and osteoporosis, it has serious side effects and contraindications. The risk of uterine cancer is ten times higher in menopausal women using oestrogen, particularly if taken alone. It is now generally combined with progesterone to lessen this risk. However, despite the mix, breast cancer rates are four times higher than normal for women using this therapy for six years or more.[4] Oestrogen is also known to increase the risk of gall bladder disease, thrombosis, phlebitis, headaches and depression. It is contraindicated for anyone suffering from liver disease, sickle cell anaemia, gall stones and diabetes, or undiagnosed abnormal vaginal bleeding.

Side effects of excess oestrogen include salt and water retention, folic acid anaemia, bloating, nausea and breast tenderness. Progesterone (given as progestins) can cause increased susceptibility to vaginal yeast and other infections, fatigue and hirsutism (excess body and facial hair).

Sedatives and tranquilisers are also prescribed for menopausal women, sometimes added to the oestrogen formula. This makes sense, in a way, because one of the side effects of HRT is depression. But recent studies have shown that women experiencing the menopause are no more inherently depressed than women at other stages of life. Rosetta Reitz, author of *Menopause: A Positive Approach*, feels that tranquilisers are prescribed primarily to keep menopausal women out of sight and out of mind and conjectures, 'Do you know what would happen if all the women between 40 and 55 started making demands? My adrenaline begins to burst forth at the excitement of the idea.'[5] Tranquilisers are also addictive, and are known to eradicate REM sleep/dreaming.

Now, let's look more closely at some of the major symptoms of the menopause, particularly those that might affect sexuality, and consider the pros and cons of HRT, plus the benefits of herbs, supplements and dietary changes.

## Hot Flushes

Three out of four women experience these; they are the most common menopausal symptom. And this symptom is the only one that is universal, occurring among women in nearly every culture. During a hot flush, a woman experiences a rush of heat to her chest, neck and face, or sometimes throughout her body. This can happen anytime, anywhere. The skin flushes, temperature increases and breathing becomes shallow. There may also be an itching sensation. As the heat passes, women often find themselves drenched in sweat, and then feel chilly and drained. These episodes may or may not be noticed by others, but most women feel deeply embarrassed by them, lest this declaration of their menopausal condition be made public. In truth, hot flushes make women painfully aware of the social conditioning that undervalues advancing age, which of course only adds to their discomfort.

Physically, hot flushes result from vasomotor instability. They originate in the temperature regulating centre of the hypothalamus, and some women find that almost anything that affects temperature, like exercise, stress, entering a cold or hot room, or even sexual arousal, can trigger a hot flush. Many women also note a strong correlation between drinking caffeinated beverages or alcohol and the onset of hot flushes. Large doses of niacin (vitamin B6) and certain drugs, such as those used to treat hypertension, are implicated. And emotional upsets can trigger hot flushes, too.

Hot flushes were once thought to be due to excess oestrogen, but are now linked to the very high levels of LH common in the menopause. However, the precise mechanism of their occurrence remains unknown.

Some women never experience hot flushes; others have them two and three times a day. Many find they only occur at night. In fact, night sweats during the menopause are very much like those postpartum, which are likewise due to hormonal change and fluctuation. Hot flushes should persist for no more than five years; the majority of women have them for several months only.

Common sense measures include layering clothing so that certain items can be shed quickly, keeping a spray bottle by the bed, in the car or at the office, having a change of sheets or towel by the bed, or using a small electric fan when feasible. Oestrogen therapy is sometimes recommended and works fairly well – but the hot flushes come right back when treatment is stopped. Tincture of motherwort, 20 drops under the tongue, is reputed to be one of the best natural remedies. Bioflavonoids added to the diet or taken as a supplement help tremendously. For additional nutritional and herbal suggestions, see the chart on page 138–9.

Apart from the nuisance, hot flushes may be the opportunity to find a new perspective. Numerous women speak of letting go to their flushes and feeling enlivened, illuminated. Some even say that hot flushes trigger intuitive insights and revelations. Barbara Raskin, author of the book, *Hot Flashes* [sic], describes her sensations as 'urgent communiques from the interior of a vast, dark continent ... fast-breaking news items from my heart of darkness'.[6] The element of darkness is strongly tied to one aspect of woman as crone: that of reaper and transformer. Perhaps hot flushes provide a metaphysical opportunity to get in touch with the shadowy side of human nature and begin to make peace with it.

Women also find that the more aware they become of the hormonal course at the menopause, the more likely they are to know a hot flush is coming. Sometimes revelations may precede the flushes and thus serve as signals to take off a sweater or turn on the fan. After all, hot flushes are symptoms of overload on the endocrine system, which is in the process of adjusting multiple physiological functions to match changed levels of oestrogen and progesterone. Overload equals altered state, and that is exactly what hot flushes represent and/or initiate.

Kitzinger likens the process of coping with hot flushes to that of coping with contractions. She recommends breathing from low in the body – down in the pelvis –

slowing down and opening up. The overall effect is somewhat erotic, right down to the rosy glow that colours a woman's face and softens her demeanour during arousal. We can use hot flushes to experience heightened awareness in a variety of ways, depending on how we focus our attention.

Just as when we try to recall our dreams and find we must write them down, there is similar benefit in recording the nature, occurrence and message (if any) in hot flushes. Raskin describes many of her flushes as cryptic enough that she can only decipher their meaning while they are still fresh. Then again, if this seems like unnecessary fuss over a simple and natural function, the sit-back-and-relax approach works just as well!

## *Vaginal and Pelvic Changes*

Besides the aforementioned vaginal dryness (typical also postpartum), tissues may thin and become easily damaged. There may be a noticeable lack of lubrication as well. None of this affects sexual libido, but can certainly influence sex itself.

These changes occur due to diminished oestrogen, which renders the vagina more alkaline than usual and hence more vulnerable to infection. Decreased oestrogen also leads to reduced vaginal and pelvic circulation, implicating the bladder and accounting for the increased incidence of urinary tract infections. Additionally, there is a reduction of transvaginal electropotential, that is, the mechanism by which water and electrolytes are conveyed across vaginal tissues.

Of all the symptoms of the menopause for which oestrogen therapy is recommended, this is the one for which it is most widely used. Oestrogen is readily absorbed

## Symptoms and treatments in menopause

| | Nutritional Supplements | Natural sources |
|---|---|---|
| Excess bleeding | Vitamin A 5,000 I.U. (International Units)<br>Vitamin C 1,000 mg<br>Iron 30 mg<br>Bioflavonoids 800 mg | hawthorn berry<br>red clover<br>dandelion root<br>shepherd's-purse |
| Hot flushes | Vitamin E 800 I.U.<br>Bioflavonoids 800 mg | motherwort<br>dong quoi<br>black cohosh<br>blue cohosh<br>false unicorn<br>fennel<br>sarsparilla<br>wild yam root<br>pomegranate |
| Vaginal changes | Vitamin E 800 I.U.<br>Bioflavonoids 800 mg<br>Evening Primrose Oil<br>Linseed Oil | blue cohosh<br>liquorice root |
| Urinary tract problems | Vitamin C 1,000–1,500 mg | uva ursi (bearberry)<br>goldenseal<br>blackberry root<br>wintergreen |
| Osteoporosis | Vitamin D 5,000 I.U.<br>Calcium Citrate 1,500 mg<br>Folid Acid 800 mcg<br>Zinc 20 mg<br>Magnesium 500 mg | oat straw<br>nettle<br>comfrey root<br>horsetail |
| Nervous irritability | Vitamin B Complex 50 mg<br>Vitamin C 1,000 mg<br>Bioflavonoids 800 mg | passionflower<br>valerian root<br>hops<br>catmint |

| Fatigue, | Vitamin B Complex 50 mg | ginger |
| depression | Vitamin C 1,000 mg | cayenne pepper |
| | Magnesium 500 mg | liqourice |
| | Potassium Aspartate 100 mg | oat straw |
| | | blessed thistle |

by vaginal tissues, and a single course of cream applied by plunger can sometimes turn things around significantly. Lubricating jelly will still be necessary, or vitamin E might be used alternatively. Seminal fluid has a positive effect on vaginal tissues, as does evening primrose oil; both contain prostaglandins which soften and condition. And orgasm itself is most beneficial: it stimulates circulation and the release of natural, soothing lubrication. According to Reitz, regular intercourse (and masturbation) make vaginal and pelvic changes at menopause 'hardly noticeable'. In fact, one study showed that weekly intercourse so increased women's oestrogen levels that many common complaints were alleviated.[7]

Continued use of oestrogen greatly increases the risk of uterine cancer, therefore natural alternatives should be tried and utilised whenever possible. Vitamin E may also be taken supplementally, at least 600 units daily. Bioflavonoids are remarkably effective for this problem; take approximately 800 mg daily. Food sources include citrus fruits, especially the inner rind, and buckwheat, which is delicious in pancakes. Herbal teas of liquorice root and blue cohosh root also help by stimulating increased production of oestrogen.

With regard to urinary tract problems, herbs like goldenseal and uva ursi (bearberry) are classic. Goldenseal contains berberine, which has antibiotic affects, and uva ursi has arbutin, a diuretic and anti-infective agent. The two can be combined and simmered slowly for tea, or taken as tincture. See the chart on page 138–9 for additional ideas.

## Osteoporosis

Osteoporosis refers to loss of bone mass, and although it occurs in men too, it is more common in our culture among women. It is linked to menopause in that oestrogen plays an important role in maintaining the structure and calcification of bone, thus a decline in this hormone is likely to precipitate the condition. There are other factors, however. Genetic predisposition figures strongly in osteoporosis, as does a diet high in salt, animal protein, caffeine, alcohol or carbonated drinks (the excess level of phosphorus directly decreases bone mass). Some authorities feel that inadequate vitamin D intake, particularly as exposure to sunlight is increasingly discouraged, may be a major, if not primary factor. This is corroborated by cross-cultural studies which show osteoporosis as far from universal in menopausal women. Some populations show no osteoporosis in women at any age, while in others, both men and women are affected, even prior to mid-life. The incidence is definitely higher in industrialised countries, among women who smoke, those with a Northern European background, those who are sedentary, and those who regularly use drugs such as steroids, diuretics, aluminium-containing antacids, thyroid supplements and anti-convulsant drugs.

The side effects of osteoporosis are worse than the condition itself. The spine tends to compress and curve, and certain bones, particularly the hips, become highly susceptible to fracture. Such injuries usually occur later, in a woman's seventies or eighties. But 30 per cent of women thus affected die of complications, and many more suffer chronic disability.

It seems obvious that diet and lifestyle are major factors in osteoporosis. What are some of the ways women can help prevent this condition from developing? For one thing, they must stop fretting about their weight, and concentrate more on nutrition. There is evidence that our ability to absorb calcium from the usual source – dairy products – actually decreases with age, thus making us more and more vulnerable. Calcium citrate, found almost exclusively in products like orange juice with added calcium, is much more readily absorbed than is calcium lactate.

Calcium is, however, just one of many nutrients essential to good health. Diet for the menopause should consist of plenty of leafy green vegetables, complex carbohydrates, low-fat foods and minimal amounts of animal protein (except fish from unpolluted waters). Especially important are trace minerals; those elements leached from the soil by commercial farming methods. Organic fruits and vegetables are sometimes as much as five times higher in food value than their commercial counterparts. It is definitely worth finding a shop that stocks organic produce.[8] See the box on page 142 for more details on nutrition in the menopause.

And then there is lifestyle to consider. Most of us spend way too much time indoors, sitting at a desk or busy with housework that keeps us just this side of aerobic, tense with the pressure of having so many things to do. This is diametrically opposed to what our lives should be about: good food, exercise and relaxation in equal measure. I think women are especially apt to deprive themselves of health-promoting necessities as they defer to the needs of others. Eventually, and sometimes with surprising swiftness, this can catch up with us.

Once again, the message is clear: the menopause is a time

## NUTRITION IN MENOPAUSE

Good nutrition is of upmost importance during the menopause. As body systems slow down, we must adapt accordingly. The digestive tract produces fewer enzymes and less hydrochloric acid as we age. Yet, many menopausal problems and complaints can be minimised or alleviated by eating the right foods. These are:

**Whole grains** These include rice, corn, wheat, barley, oats, rye, millet, buckwheat, brown rice and wild rice. These stabilise blood sugar levels and can reduce sugar cravings. They help prevent diabetes, and may also protect against cancer of the colon as they are high in fibre. Eat freely of these, and aim for some variety each week.

**Legumes** Legumes are various kinds of peas and beans, such as lentils, kidney beans, black beans, chick peas, pinto beans, white beans, split peas, etc. They are very high in protein and fibre, and digest slowly, making them especially appropriate for older women. Problems with gas can be alleviated by slow and thorough cooking, or by eating small amounts.

**Vegetables** These provide a full range of vitamins and minerals. The dark green, orange and red varieties are high in vitamin A, which has been shown to protect against cancer of the breast and cervix, as well as immunological disease. Vitamin C has similar benefits, and helps prevent excessive bleeding at menopause if combined with iron and bioflavonoids. Good sources of C include peppers, potatoes, tomatoes, broccoli, cabbage, peas, parsley and kale. Vegetables also provide important minerals like calcium, magnesium, iron, and trace elements if grown organically. Onions and garlic help lower serum cholesterol, which reduces the risk of strokes and heart attacks. Seaweeds like kelp are high in iodine, which promotes healthy thyroid function.

**Fruits** Fruits also provide a wide range of vitamins and minerals. They are particularly high in potassium, which serves to regulate blood pressure. Potassium also helps prevent fatigue associated with menopause. Especially rich sources include bananas, berries, melons, grapefruit, peaches and apricots. High fibre is another bonus because it can minimise constipation. Pineapple and papaya specifically aid digestion by breaking down proteins.

**Seeds and nuts** These are good sources of protein, but are very high in fat and calories and thus should be eaten sparingly. Magnesium, potassium and calcium are quite concentrated in nuts and seeds, particularly almonds, sunflower seeds, pumpkin seeds and sesame seeds. They digest best if eaten raw.

**Fish and poultry** In terms of animal protein, these are preferred sources. Red meats are high in fat, hard to digest, and often laden with hormones and preservatives. Fish is an outstanding source of linoleic acid, which is said to help with dryness of the hair, skin and vaginal tissues (this may also be taken supplementally as linseed oil/capsules).

Foods to avoid include the following:

**Salt** In excess, this mineral can exacerbate bloating, high blood pressure, heart disease, and osteoporosis.

**Sugar** Too much sugar can accelerate diabetes, deplete essential vitamins and minerals and cause stress, anxiety, and vulnerability to infection.

**Caffeine** Excess caffeine can cause mood swings, interfere with carbohydrate metabolism, exacerbate hot flushes and worsen osteoporosis.

**Alcohol** Alcohol has similar effects to those of caffeine. It also disrupts the liver's ability to metabolise hormones, intensifying menopausal complaints.

**Fats** Saturated fats, found in dairy products and meats, are especially bad for menopausal women in that they link to heart disease, high blood pressure, stroke, and cancer of the ovaries, breasts and uterus.

Adapted from *The Menopause Self Help Book*, by Susan Lark, M.D. and published by Celestial Arts, Berkeley, 1990

for realignment. And rather than wait until the time is upon us, we should begin to pay better attention to our health and well-being straight away.

In her bestseller, *The Silent Passage*, Gail Sheehy portrays the common complaints of the menopause as universally disruptive and virtually incapacitating. And yet, numerous studies show that most women have very little trouble. Often, fear intensifies or exacerbates initial symptoms just enough to drive women to seek hormone replacement, much as fear in labour makes contractions infinitely harder to handle and leads women to ask for drugs. Ask your own mother or older sisters what menopause was like for them, as patterns and severity of symptoms tend to run in families. Even more important are the coping mechanisms your female relations used: what worked and what didn't. I was relieved when my mother told me that the menopause had been a breeze for her; she had had hot flushes at night occasionally, and that was about it. If, however, your mother responds with a horror story, don't panic. Get the entire picture, complete with medical interventions, and add lifestyle factors too before jumping to any conclusions.

## SEX DURING THE MENOPAUSE

What's sex like at this time? Reports range wildly, with everything from blooming desire to total disinterest. From Marjorie:

Looking back, I think my moods had a lot to do with it. I never really let go of having a second child, even though the years went by and nothing happened. Then menopause put an end to that dream, and I cried and raged at my husband, to the point that *he* called the doctor for sedatives! I tried oestrogen for a while, but just got more depressed. I wanted absolutely nothing to do with Blake ... I acted as though I blamed him for everything. Actually, I guess I did: when I wanted kids early in our marriage, he wasn't ready, and then we had to wait so long for our son. Anyway, my hot flushes were awful, they happened to me everywhere and often made me cry. Sometimes I'd come home and scream in the closet, when no one was there.

We didn't have sex, except once in a while when I felt I could stomach it, like once a month or so. After it [menopause] was all over, though, I got my drive back all right ... I only wish my husband had. Things are different between us and I know we'll never be the same.

Quite the opposite experience, from Gerry:

Menopause was liberation for me. I didn't expect it, but so it was. No more worry about birth control ... after four children, free at last! And by then, the youngest was almost full grown. I took classes at the local college, art and creative writing. I felt so good to finally be able to pursue my dreams. And sex, well, we reached new heights with it. My drive became more intense, my confidence increased, my husband loved it! He began to take more time with me, feeding my senses and enjoying *my* rhythms. We were really on a par.

Gerry's story is actually a bit more postmenopausal. Here is Elaine's tale, from deep in the thick of it:

I welcomed menopause; I wasn't afraid because I'd learned to trust my body over the years and felt ready for whatever it had in store for me. The intensity of the hot flushes threw me at first, but I began to see them as a sort of energy release. When I looked at menopause as a transition to my wiser, seasoned self, I decided that with every flush, I'd let something go — some obligation to someone else's priorities, some outdated idea of myself, some old wound. It was exhilarating to do this – really a rush! Sometimes I'd flush during intercourse, usually at the beginning of arousal, and I'd use the energy as sort of a boost to my passion. My partner had no complaints. He didn't always know what was happening, but I think it took the edge off my sharpness at times. Menopausal women are so powerful – I think men can be intimated by the change. For us, sex was the bridge.

Diane says of her experience with Elsa:

I was in menopause before my partner, by about a year or so. So we both experienced hot flushes over a period of time, although hers were the most intense. It was fun, really . . . wonderful to have genuine support and understanding. The minor inconveniences some women speak of, like vaginal dryness – well, applying oils to each other became a special part of our sexual pleasure.

And lastly, a classically mixed response:

I grieved during menopause – I hate to admit it, because I consider myself a liberated woman. But who wants to grow old? What woman wants to lose her looks? This deeply affected my self-confidence and desire for sex. I was afraid I'd lose my partner, and so was scared to be vulnerable in bed. When the hot flushes were most intense, a period of three months or so, we stopped making love. My vagina felt different too, dry and very tender. In retrospect, I think I was testing my partner, and lo and behold, after it was all over, he was still there. Then my desire skyrocketed, and I took hold of the situation.

Thus far, we've considered menopause only as a natural phenomenon. When it is surgically induced, as by hysterectomy, the experience is entirely different. Instead of a gradual decline in hormonal levels, the system is thrown into shock and withdrawal.

In 1987, 800,000 American women had hysterectomies, and up to one third have been called unnecessary. 'American women are up to four times more likely to have hysterectomies than women of other industrialized countries.'[9] In the UK, one out of five women who reach seventy-five will have had their uterus removed (Kitzinger). Although some doctors truly feel that women not intending to have children and at risk from pelvic diseases are safer without their reproductive organs, such a view totally discounts the physical difficulties and emotional trauma women tend to experience when this transition occurs so abruptly. Even when there are clear indications for surgery, loss of her reproductive organs can cause a woman to sink into depression, and undergo a classic process of grieving (see Chapter Eight).

There are four general indications for hysterectomy: 1) cancer of the reproductive organs; 2) severe infection of the Fallopian tubes, uterus or ovaries that cannot be controlled; 3) extremely large fibroid tumours; 4) uncontrollable uterine bleeding unresponsive to D and C or any other remedy. These conditions, however, account for only 12 per cent of all hysterectomies. If a woman requires surgery for either of the latter two, the ovaries need not necessarily be removed, particularly if the woman is over forty, when the risk of ovarian cancer drops to one per cent. Subtotal hysterectomy, whereby the ovaries (or some part thereof) are saved, is a better solution. Even a small portion of a single ovary will continue rhythmic hormonal production. And if the difficulty is fibroids alone, a myomectomy permits surgical removal of the fibroid while saving the uterus. Although fibroid tissue tends to grow back, myomectomy is the best solution for a woman whose fibroid has grown cumbersome (they can reach a weight of 7 stones) and who still wants children.

Sex for the woman who has undergone complete hysterectomy is apt to be distressing both physically and emotionally. Annette recalls: 'I felt empty, like I had nothing to offer anymore. My muscles were all shot and soft – my vagina was foreign territory to me and I wasn't sure I wanted to get to know it again. To have to face the fact that I'd never have a child and would never give birth was unspeakably painful to me, and wiped the magic from sex and my body for a very long time.' Another woman reports: 'The inside of me felt all stopped up and rigid – like a dead-end, literally. I had periodic bleeding at first, which was normal, they said. Even though it was scary, I welcomed it – at least *something* was coming out of me! When I bled, I found that I could cry. After it stopped, I turned my sadness inward until I healed.'

On the other side, here's an account from Mandy: 'I had suffered so tremendously with endometriosis and uterine infection that the decision for hysterectomy came as a relief. I wasn't sure I wanted kids anyway, and now the matter was settled. But I noticed a funny thing: for months after the surgery, I still felt a rhythm, a ghost cycle of sorts. I didn't know how much that rhythm had become a part of me, wracked with pain as I was.'

Some women notice a change in orgasms after hysterectomy. The deeper contractions felt in the uterus, or the stimulation of the cervix that some women find pleasurable, are no longer part of the picture. This sort of sexual crisis necessitates refocusing and reconditioning oneself to find satisfaction in other pleasure centres. With abrupt withdrawal of oestrogen, even the clitoris may atrophy, but ongoing stimulation via masturbation generally serves to compensate.

Sometimes, though, symptoms of surgically induced menopause are so severe as to necessitate HRT, at least for a time. Many women try to taper the hormones down to a minimal level by their late forties, and discontinue them in their fifties. Others choose to stay on them indefinitely.

Brooke Medicine Eagle, Native American writer on women's health issues, has spoken at length on the meaning of the menopause. She speculates that perhaps hysterectomy is an opportunity for certain women to assume mature leadership roles traditionally held by their elders. Due to our longstanding deficit in women's wisdom, she sees the urgent need for its resurgence necessitating input from younger women (albeit by the extreme of surgery). The menopause, whenever it occurs, marks a time when precious menstrual fluid, 'wise blood', is retained for heightened awareness, and greater social authority. Postmenopausal women of the 'Grandmother Lodge' are thus accorded the deepest respect and the highest honour.[10]

### CELEBRATING 'THE CHANGE'

Of course, in Native American and many other indigenous cultures, women at menopause are acknowledged by rituals which help them make their transition more gracefully and completely. As was mentioned earlier, the menopause in our culture is often accompanied by not a little grief. What sort of ritual might we employ to help us acknowledge this sense of loss while at the same time exploring the great potential of this transition?

Most menopausal rituals naturally incorporate some

way of letting go of the past and welcoming new responsibilities. Here are a few examples. The first ritual has women gather around a fire (or it may be a symbolic candle) and take turns, one by one, giving up some fear, grief or self-limiting belief to be consumed by the flame. If the fire is large enough, each woman can actually throw in a piece of wood, paper or cloth – something to symbolise that which is being surrendered. At the same time, each woman speaks of what she has learned in life, her most profound lessons, as well as that which she has yet to accomplish. The woman next to her then acknowledges what she has said, and charges her with the responsibility of nurturing life via her special gifts and vision.

In essence, the transition to cronehood signifies a time when women transmute their personal pursuits and the inherent demands of child bearing to become 'Keepers of the Law'. Their role shifts from nurturing their immediate families to caring for humanity, bringing to bear on society at large their seasoned sense of justice and harmony. The word crone is, in fact, similar in derivation to crown, signifying leadership. Even the word hag, which has such derogatory meaning in our culture, comes from the Greek 'hagia', meaning 'a holy one'.

In this respect, it's best to have women of all ages present at a menopause celebration: crones, mothers and maidens. For this ritual, everyone gathers around a large bowl or pot of water. Each has a cup, and each takes a turn to dip and drink, saying 'I accept the wisdom of ages past.' Then the crones form an inner circle and one by one, each says what she has learned in life and names the wisdom she still needs or the things she must do to complete her life's mission. As she finishes speaking, another crone dips water and gives it to her to sip, saying, 'Take from the wisdom of the ages the means to fulfil your destiny.' Or, 'Shed the skin that has become too tight for you and be born anew.'

When the crones are done, the other women may ask them for whatever they need to grow and be wise. As each one finishes, the elder woman to whom she is speaking gives her water to sip and repeats the blessing given above.

Although these rituals work best in groups, the same acts of letting go, naming accomplishments and identifying the keys to one's destiny can be done in solitude. Use a candle, the water, or both, and be sure to voice your thoughts: the power of the spoken word is great. If menopausal symptoms ebb and flow over a period of years, it may be necessary to do this ritual a number of times.

### SEX IN LATER YEARS

Just how satisfying and wonderful a woman's sex life will be once she is past the menopause depends largely on how well she retains her self-respect and enthusiasm for living. Against all the odds, she must define herself, her continued growth and new found authority as valuable, despite society's views to the contrary. So pervasive is the image of older women as used up 'biddies' that this task can be difficult indeed. As our culture defines women primarily by physical beauty and their ability to serve others, it's no wonder many suffer as they age, their children leave home and family obligations lessen.

One of our finest references for tracking demeaning attitudes towards older women is Barbara Walker's, *The Crone*. Walker shows that in pre-Christian culture throughout the world, the mythic triumvirate of virgin, mother, and crone reigned supreme. Christianity virtually annihilated the latter, retaining only the more benign and readily controlled figures of maiden and mother.

What made the crone so threatening? In the Hindu

tradition, she was known as Kali the Destroyer – not that she was maliciously violent or spiteful, but she did possess a natural instinct to terminate anything that had exhausted its usefulness in order that it might be transformed to something new. Accordingly, her power was tremendous. In myth after myth, the crone persona proved stronger than any god. As the Teutonic Elli, she conquered Thor, the god of strength. As Celtic Morgan Le Fay (or Morgan the Fate), she had the power to humble and tame all men. As Atropos the Cutter (Greek), she snipped the thread of every life.

The aspect of the crone most frightening to men is her power to reject, to refuse to care for their individual concerns and to care instead for society at large or for fundamental principles of justice and evolution. Women's power to say 'no,' and to see and serve a higher moral code or natural law, is what men have sought so desperately to obliterate. In the witch hunts of the twelfth to sixteenth centuries, millions – yes, millions – of women were victims of torture and burning.[11] Even today, if the counsel of our female elders was sought, it would undoubtedly be in opposition to male predilections for war, aggression, domination, wastefulness, and the irrational justification of these.

Fortunately, at least some contemporary cultures hold elder women in great esteem. In Japan, a woman reaches the highest and most venerated stage of maturity at age 61, an event marked by ceremony. In some North and South American Indian cultures, postmenopausal women acquire special status and privileges in the community as they transcend menstrual taboos. In China too, elder woman are venerated and accorded the highest respect.

But beyond honour and veneration, elder women in matriarchal cultures of the Middle East and Egypt had opportunities to perform society's most important and

challenging roles. They served as doctors, midwives, sur-
geons, health care advisors, authorities on child rearing
and sexuality. As scribes, they recorded for both temple
and court, maintained vital records and histories, set up
calendars and official tables of weights and measures,
transcribed and edited scriptures, and ran libraries. They
were generally busier in later years than they were during
the child bearing cycle. Mythology reminds us that important inventions in the fields of medicine, nutrition and food
preparation were made by women in their 'years of
wisdom'.[12]

Besides earthly responsibilities, elder women had metaphysical charges too. They took care of most religious rites
and official ceremonies, from birth to death. In terms of the
afterlife, it was generally believed that one was taken up in
the arms of the Mother, rather than, as by Christian tenets,
to the bosom [?] of the Father. In Buddhist/Tantric traditions, three classes of priestess – yogini, matri and dakini –
represented the virgin, mother and crone. Dakini (the
crone) literally means skywalker; devoted to the destructive
aspect, she prepared the dying for death, worked with
bereaved families and administered last rites. She also
knew the way into the spirit realm, and could be either
fierce or gentle, depending on the dying one's behaviour in
life and lessons still to be learned in crossing over.

Similarly, Luisa Francia calls the crone the 'goddess of
the crossroads' who can hinder or block one's way, kill or
allow one to pass. Stories and tales from all over the world
show that the path to knowledge or true love inevitably
leads through the old woman, the witch, or the woods-
woman. She may appear to be fragile or foolish so that no
one takes her seriously, then suddenly she shows her
power. In Syria, the crone was portrayed as the huge-eyed
goddess Mari, who searched men's souls. The Christian

adaptation of this was found in the figure of Aynat, the all-seeing Evil Eye. To a large extent, the ability to look through the veil that hid the future was the province of the crone, although superstition readily led to her being blamed for events she had merely foretold.

Yet another mythic figure symbolising the power of the crone is Shakti, an amalgam of queenly strength, intelligence, grace, and sexuality. (Shakti, in fact, translates directly to the word vulva.) Across the board, crone figures possess a strong sexual dimension, which clearly fits with what we know of the postmenopausal increase in androgens/testosterone. It's not the sensuality of the crone that is frightening to men, but the combination of sexual power with emotional and intellectual discernment.

Authors Rhonda L. Winn and Niles Newton compiled some fascinating research in their paper, 'Sexuality in Aging: A Study of 106 Cultures'. In most indigenous societies, older women were found to be extremely interested in sex. In 22 per cent of those surveyed, women became markedly less inhibited with regard to sexual conversation, sexual humour and sexual gestures as they aged. Seventy per cent of societies analysed by the authors, such as the Loredu of South Africa, the Woges of New Guinea, the Trobriand and Eastern Islanders, showed older women having much younger men as sexual partners. Even very old women, described by observers as 'toothless and decrepit', were able to obtain young and attractive boys as lovers. Often, older women played the role of sexual initiator and instructor.

Many of these women displayed a range of sexually suggestive behaviour, from copulatory movements while dancing to touching or grabbing men's genitals (or their own) in public, often with a touch of humour. Similarly, they showed a fondness for risqué jokes and anecdotes.

Why does this occur? Apart from hormonal changes, the open sexuality of older women is a natural expression of power in cultures where they maintain dominant social roles. It is noteworthy that in those societies in which sexual activity is inhibited in the aged, younger individuals tend to view the old as undesirable, or even repulsive.[13]

This has been more or less the case in the United States. According to the Consumers' Union survey in 1984 entitled *Love, Sex and Aging*, some 4,296 respondents agreed that society saw them as nonsexual. Only 65 per cent of women over 70 were sexually active. Of course, we have the phenomenon of women outliving their husbands and struggling awkwardly to find new partners, overshadowed by the fear of sexually transmitted diseases. But as the baby boomer generation ages, their characteristic pursuit of self-realisation will most likely extend to enduring sexual expression. And as for women outliving men, the authors of *Life Trends* predict that we will see increasing acceptance of lesbian coupling as a lifestyle option for older women (not to mention women in general).[14]

On the other hand, the longer we live, the more we as couples will spend an unprecedented number of years together. Rosalie Gilford, sociologist, sums it up this way: 'Never in history have the lives of husbands and wives remained interwoven in intact marriages so long as to encounter the constellation of life-changing events that the last stages of the marital career now bring.' Unsettling discoveries of differences may arise for couples in these circumstances, particularly if their lives have been organised around child rearing. All of this is, of course, compounded by hormonally-induced role reversal. But if a couple is able to embrace these changes by having the woman take more initiative while her partner assumes a more receptive role, a natural and practical sort of androgyny may ensue.

In bed, interesting possibilities arise. The combination of men's slower arousal times and women's increased aggressiveness can lead to long, drawn-out, even ritualistic lovemaking, with women in the lead. As Charlotte reports:

> James and I have been together for 43 years. We have four grown children and seven grandchildren. I suppose our sex life in the early years was like most others – James came quickly, was a little lacking in touch and timing, and my orgasms were sporadic, at best. But I always loved to masturbate, and now, with the standards changing as they are, I find I can talk to him about the intimate details of my body. At first, I think I talked to help cover his embarrassment at slowing down – complimenting him and teaching him at the same time, you might say. But oh, the times we have now! Why, it's hours of pleasure for both of us!

Angelina has a different sort of story:

> After I went through 'the change' I felt so different! Drier, sometimes, and quite unsure of myself. But I wasn't the only one! Robert took longer to come around, and wanted to spend more time touching than ever before. At first, we were rather confused by all this, but eventually, our affection and companionship deepened, and we felt more alike, more in harmony with one another.

These changes are certainly natural, but tame compared to those of some women who go all out for sex in their later years. Jeanne reports:

> I'm almost 70 now, but I can't say that I feel old. Oh,

sometimes I have days when I take it a bit slower, but I generally feel vigorous and self-possessed. I've had a career, you know, and children of whom I'm exceedingly proud – grandchildren, too!

Menopause was tempestuous for me because my life was so hectic then, and frankly, my marriage suffered. But a few years after, when I was about 58, something came over me and I felt this strength and certitude in myself, which reached full bloom in the bedroom. I had always liked sex, and had orgasms easily. But now, there was another dimension. I'd lift off, into my own thoughts and imagination, and experience elemental shifts in my consciousness, almost on a regular basis. You know how things are when you're swept away completely by orgasm, with no idea how you got there? Well, now I seemed to have ready access to those planes – freedom to fly, I called it. Trying to account for it, well, my life was so simple, compared to my child rearing years, and I kept myself challenged and growing with personal pursuits. Really, this was quite the opposite of what I expected sex to be like at this time of my life!

This account ties directly back to the power and authority of the crone, and raises the final question: how can we realise the full dimensions of cronehood in our present day society? Or, to put it in Jeanne's terminology, where do we find the freedom to fly, to traverse the realms of our awareness with ease and confidence?

One approach is to act on our natural authority at this stage, seeking out opportunities to 'sit in council' and employ our wisdom. Brooke Medicine Eagle speaks of the 'Law of Good Relationship', whereby the grandmothers had the final say in setting right any cultural imbalance. For example, if a chief was not leading the tribe in such a way

that people had food, clear water and shelter, the grandmothers asked for someone new. Or if in times of war, a
chief instigated such animosity that attacks disrupted the
tribe's well-being, the grandmothers might redirect him or
demand that he be removed. Today, women's groups rally
around the issues of peace, the environment, education and
healthcare, and older women need to assume their natural
role of leadership and let their voices be heard. Deliberately
forming an elder women's group, then finding focus within
it – there may be several subgroups with distinct projects –
is another possibility. In this vein, Kitzinger describes
postmenopausal women in peasant societies of China and
Spain, for example, as 'political dynamos, wheeling and
dealing, plotting and scheming'.

There is, however, a twist on the matter of responsibility,
tied to the psychological implications of loss. Loss of youth,
loss of children (once out of the home), loss of one's own
parents, and ultimately, loss of interest in maintaining 'the
nest', may lead older women to weed out their possessions
and pare down life to the essentials. Although psychiatrists
may categorise these acts as symptoms of 'postmenopausal
depression', such nest-destroying behaviour is actually quite
normal. Finding the courage and vision to walk away from
former entanglements, or seek a simpler way of living can
enable a woman to establish a new and necessary equilibrium.

Thus, in keeping with the idea of role reversal at the
menopause, a woman who has played an active role in the
world might even choose to go into retreat, finding balance
in spiritual pursuits and perhaps in solitude. Whatever we
choose, the need for radical departure from obligatory
roles as a means of expressing one's inner authority is key.
And it is in this framework that sexual fulfilment will be
realised.

1. Wilson, Robert A., *Feminine Forever* (New York, Pocket Books, 1971)
2. Reuben, David, *Everything You Always Wanted to Know About Sex but Were Afraid to Ask* (New York, Bantam Books, 1971)
3. Kitzinger, Sheila, *Woman's Experience of Sex* (New York, Penguin Books, 1985)
4. 'Menopause: Baby Boomers' Next Step', *The Los Angeles Times* (December 1989)
5. Reitz, Rosetta, *Menopause: A Positive Approach* (New York, Penguin Books, 1979)
6. Raskin, Barbara, *Hot Flashes* (New York, St. Martin's Press, 1987)
7. Culter, Winnifred, *Love Cycles* (New York, Villard Books, 1991)
8. 'Why Organic Food Matters,' *The Journal of Sustainable Agriculture* (Vol. 1:1, 1985)
9. Jovanovic, Lois and Subak-Sharpe, Genell, *Hormones: The Woman's Answer Book* (New York, Ballantine Books, 1987)
10. Taylor, Dena, *Red Flower: Rethinking Menstruation* (Freedom, California, Crossing Press, 1988)
11. Ehrenreich, Barbara and English, Deirdre, *Witches, Midwives and Nurses*: A history of women healers (New York, Feminist Press, 1973)
12. Walker, Barbara, *The Crone* (San Francisco, Harper & Row, 1985)
13. Winn, Rhonda L. and Newton, Niles, 'Sexuality in Aging: A Study of 106 Cultures', *Archives of Sexual Behavior* (Vol. II:4, 1982)
14. Gerber, Jerry; Wolff, Janet; Klores, Walter; Brown, Gene, *Life Trends* (New York, Avon Books, 1989)

# 7

# Sexual dysfunction
# and abuse

How does a chapter on sexual dysfunction fit into a book on women's sexual rhythms? I'd venture to say that the vast majority of women today have passed through some phase of sexual dysfunction. Of course, it all depends on how we define this. I think sexual dysfunction occurs when we have lost the ability to be sexually self-determined; and have more or less sexual activity than suits us, whether by denial, inhibition or compulsion. For example, we may overindulge in sex as an addiction, or may find ourselves unable to relate sexually due to unresolved trauma or abuse in our relationships.

We touched only briefly on abuse issues in Chapter Three, as regards pregnancy's potential to trigger recognition and acknowledgement of injuries long forgotten. In fact, it seems that abuse of women is so widespread that the real object is to be able to remember, to dredge from the depths what lies buried. How do we remember abuse?

Workshops on the subject are increasingly available,

turning up on seemingly unrelated conference agendas, or community college calendars. Women often attend out of curiosity, feeling somewhat bewildered as to why they are there, but by the session's end may find they recall some incident long repressed. There is a growing climate of acceptance as regards the significance of abuse on a woman's sexuality and self-esteem, her ability to mother and to form and sustain healthy relationships. Women are at last being encouraged to acknowledge this sort of experience rather than minimise it, as was previously expected.

## SEX AND PHYSICAL ABUSE

Lest there be any doubt as to cultural attitudes surrounding abuse, our criminal justice system has shown great reluctance to prosecute abusers, particularly on the basis of children's testimony. That females are somehow responsible for their own abuse is deeply ingrained all around the world. Women's bodies have been categorically presented as sinful and unclean, thus women are veiled, mutilated by clitorectomy, and sold millions of pounds worth of feminine hygiene sprays, deodorised panty-liners and so on. Jurors may still believe that if a girl over the age of seven or so is abused, it's partially because she has behaved seductively, albeit unintentionally. When women are raped, they must face similar assumptions that they may be at least partially to blame. Women are grilled as to what they wore or how they behaved when the crime occurred, as though capable of playing accessory roles.

Rape is an ugly and difficult issue. One thing is clear: rape happens, and often – once every six minutes in the United States, once every ninety seconds in South Africa. Women need to take measures to protect themselves. They need to be realistic about their vulnerability, and avoid situations that might jeopardise their well-being until the world is a safer place for women in general. In the end, even if a rape case goes to trial and a woman is vindicated, she nevertheless bears scars of her violation that demand deep healing and retribution. She experiences a significant loss of herself, and must spend much time and energy making up for it.

Women who have been violently accosted and raped can't get the memory out of their minds. But when a woman is raped by either someone she's dating or her own husband or partner, it is somewhat easier to forget, to repress. One way to check into this for yourself is to answer the following questions. Have you ever been forced to have sex against your will? Have you ever been forcibly restrained or held down for sex while clearly indicating you wanted to be free? If so, you have indeed been raped.

The questions to unearth sexual abuse by a stranger, acquaintance or relative are more subtle and numerous. Have you ever been tricked into an intimate situation you did not desire? Has anyone ever touched you intimately and against your will? Do you have a lot of trouble surrendering during intercourse? Do you hate being touched? Do you have trouble setting boundaries with others? Do you find great difficulty in trusting others, especially members of the opposite sex? Do you continually find yourself stuck in relationships? Have you a chronic illness, particularly gynaecological problems? Do you often feel outside yourself when you have sex? If you have even an inkling of recollection, contact a support organisation and find someone to talk to.

Sometimes, memories of abuse are triggered by stressful situations. Pregnancy is one example, as intense hormonal changes and complex social factors tend deeply to affect personality. Other catalysts may include bitter arguments with loved ones, death or injury to a loved one, injury to oneself, and (yes, you guessed it) sexual activity. In short, anything that causes us to feel pushed to our limits and vulnerable is apt to release the subconscious and bring unpleasant memories to the surface.

This woman's story serves to illustrate:

We were making love and were hot into it – my husband pushed me over on my side to enter me from behind, which I really didn't want when suddenly, something just went off inside me and I panicked. Not in my head but in my heart, my gut, there was this constriction, this fear. I knew it had nothing to do with him, but I couldn't deny the feeling. Actually, I had noticed this before in other situations with men when I felt them manipulating me. I noticed the same fear and this feeling of terror, just below the surface. Part of me would freeze up and go limp, as if in survival mode.

Finally, through hypnosis, I remembered some friend of my uncle forcing me to let him play with my nipples, show him my backside and let him finger me, just a little on the outside. That's all that ever happened, but I responded in that same way back then – I froze, stood still, felt very much in danger but powerless to cry out. I felt totally humiliated, like I was no good, dirty, and it was all my fault.

Once I got over this, I could see what was happening with my husband. Whenever he was forceful with me, even if it was really okay, I just froze up – I couldn't help it. And if I let him go ahead anyway, I had those same feelings of self-loathing. We had some stuff to work out, I can tell you!

We'll look more at how abuse affects sexuality in a moment. But first, we have yet another list to trigger associations. Here are some typical characteristics and modes of behaviour of women who have been abused.

- Describes self as never having been a child
- Extremely concerned with control
- Overly willing to expose genitals to others
- Unexplained pain with intercourse
- Extreme ideas about sexuality
- Hypersensitive to touch
- Repeatedly exploited by others in relationship
- Deeply estranged from family
- General feeling of being 'under it'
- Detaches from self and others
- Nothing ever wrong with life, always neutral
- Childlike behaviour, dress or appearance
- Unkempt personal appearance
- Sexually exploitive dress
- Chaotic surroundings and habits
- Overly controlled surroundings or habits
- No personal boundaries
- No trust
- Anger inappropriate or out of proportion to the situation
- Inability to appreciate others
- Blind adoration of others
- Fanatic religious or philosophical beliefs
- Jumps into situations and to conclusions
- Difficulty with decision-making[1]

From this list alone, it's pretty easy to extrapolate sexual response patterns. Women who have suffered abuse show a full range of sexual behaviour, from total frigidity to compulsive sexual activity and/or display. The latter may seem a bit surprising, but it's almost as if the victim is saying, 'See, I'm so sexual and out there with it that no one can take control of me – I'm in charge.' This attitude generally precludes the surrender that leads to orgasm; it almost certainly precludes intimacy. Actually, this is the quintessentially masculine approach of using sex primarily for self-gratification, without placing it in the context of a relationship. Women who have been abused may unconsciously reject their feminine vulnerability to be more on a par with their oppressor. Clarrise related, 'In retrospect, it's like I bought into the beliefs of the man who abused me. My cunt was just a cunt, and I used it that way, keeping myself separate from it, using it as much as I could to prove the point that it was not me, I didn't have to be connected.'

It is easy to correlate discomfort with touch or intercourse to sexual abuse, but the psychological damage that leads to increased vulnerability to disease, accidents and career instability is more complex. Many characteristics of abusees are in fact contradictory, though notably extreme. The manic-depressive personality often correlates to a history of sexual abuse.

Besides the obvious means of physical or sexual abuse, there are many other ways or instances in which women may feel abused. How many of us, for example, have felt violated during a gynaecological examination, as procedures were done or tools used forcibly to examine us when we clearly were not ready? Or perhaps we've felt patronised after the examination, as our intimate questions and concerns were brushed aside or ridiculed. Women often report feeling abused by birthing procedures that involve overuse of technology or invasion of privacy. These sorts of abuse, less clear-cut because so widespread and culturally acceptable, nevertheless affect women in characteristic fashion: self-esteem and self-worth are diminished, personal boundaries are lost or disrupted, and sexual response and satisfaction are likely to be affected.

In my many years of practising women's health, I've had ample experience with women suffering from what is commonly known as vaginism, or vaginismus: an uncontrollable contraction of the vaginal muscles whenever penetration is attempted. This is especially sad to see in very young women, particularly if the cause is that their first gynaecological examination was so rough that they now find it difficult to have intercourse, let alone regular checkups. Of course, vaginismus is also a classic sign of sexual abuse.

When working with a woman who has this problem, I go out of my way to put her in control. I use a very small speculum, for example, and have her insert it herself. Sometimes this is not possible, and we need to start from the most basic point of having her put her finger inside to find the involuntary contraction response so she can work directly on relaxing the muscles. Of course this takes time, but her resulting sense of mastery as she begins to overcome this fear makes it completely worthwhile. She probably will not be cured of her condition, and may in fact find that the same involuntary response occurs the next time she tries to have intercourse. But at least she may feel confident enough to communicate with her partner and discuss her needs and her fears.

Otherwise she may find it possible to have sex only by detaching herself. She may enjoy clitoral stimulation and orgasm but, feeling herself close as she is entered, will then pull back in silence and shame. This is tragic because the pattern perpetuates itself, and the woman remains a victim.

Classic therapeutic techniques for vaginismus include

behavioural approaches of densitisation. A woman is asked to relax thoroughly and then imagine, step-by-step, the stages of intercourse while trying to stay open as much as possible. Sometimes plastic dilators are used by the woman herself to simulate penetration by another in conjunction with visualisation. Other techniques include 'flooding', that is, bringing to mind all her worries and fears while allowing penetration, sometimes involving the woman's partner in clinical practice.[2] The trouble with these approaches is that they may not allow her the necessary release of emotion, particularly of anger.

Besides, penetration is not the be-all and end-all of sexual pleasure for women that it is for men. Penetration affords very little stimulation to the clitoris; thus it follows that women do not necessarily need penetration to find sexual fulfilment.

The best approach for a woman struggling with vaginismus is to talk with her partner and reach an exploration agreement. That is, the two of them agree to let her take the lead in showing him all the finer points of what is arousing to her – her particulars of pleasure. She can first show him exactly what she does when she masturbates, where and how she likes to be touched. Then she can guide him to try the same – only that, and no more.

Sheila Kitzinger has described this technique step-by-step, and recommends that from this point, penetration occur only with the woman's own finger as mutual pleasuring continues. The woman's partner can climax outside her, in her hand or between her legs, wherever feels okay with her. Above all, both she and her partner should agree in advance that she will be free to stop the process at any time. Eventually, it may be his finger inside her or his penis, but she must always be in control and in charge of the pace, doing as much as or as little as seems right to her each time. Some women find they actually prefer sex without penetration, and the couple then needs to work out some mutually acceptable arrangement.

In a similar vein are the traumas attendant to delivering a baby with an unplanned or undesired episiotomy. As discussed in Chapter Four, there are certain practical considerations in healing the vaginal area when there has been injury or trauma, and most women who have had repair have a certain amount of hesitation the first time they have sex. But some feel more than hesitation. The psychological trauma of episiotomy may link to a feeling of violation. Women speak of being mutilated, changed, no longer themselves. The net result is similar to that of sexual abuse; the sufferer feels shame, guilt and inadequacy for having been contaminated/affected, as if it was all her fault.

Working through a negative cycle of sexual identification requires, in most cases, an opportunity to relive the key event in vivid and clear detail. This should trigger the original reaction, which may then be transformed into something more self-affirming. Unfortunately, many women never have an opportunity to get past their anger. Finding so little external validation for what they feel, they direct their fury and frustration at themselves, in self-immolation. The healing process must also incorporate an objective look at the situation. With episiotomy, for example, documentation is readily available on its exorbitant overuse in the United States as opposed to European countries, not to mention the lack of practitioner training in America in skills to maintain an intact perineum. A woman needs to share with her partner her fear, shame, anger and her need for both reassurance and enough autonomy to find her own way to heal. If there is anything we health workers ought to know by now, it's that whatever happens to a woman's body also happens to her spirit. She may temporarily separate these so that they may better reunite, but she cannot (and must never be expected to) divorce the two.

## EMOTIONAL ABUSE

Emotional abuse is certainly a component of physical abuse. When a woman is raped, she suffers much more than physical injury; the comments and insults of her attacker have as far-reaching effects as the degradation of her body. Girls who are victims of incest feel the psychological manipulation to be just as devastating as the physical violation.

But emotional abuse may also stand alone, manifesting itself in patterns of relationship that tend to repeat themselves. Again, society has put women at such a disadvantage when it comes to self-preservation that we must deliberately steer clear of guilt and blame in examining our susceptibility to emotional violation. Then again, as both sexes are indeed vulnerable to the effects of emotional abuse, we must look beyond misogyny for other causes.

We can, I think, trace vulnerability back to early childhood experience, particularly with regard to bonding and attachment. According to Avodah Offit, M.D., author of *The Sexual Self*, sexual behaviour is very much influenced by the degree to which we've bonded to another in infancy, which in turn affects how well we deal with the anxiety of separation. As stated earlier, if we are kept close and secure when small, we become more comfortable with ourselves and better able to tolerate being alone. If, as claimed by William James, 'The greatest terror of infancy is solitude', then perhaps we need to re-examine the manner in which we gain independence. In an era of putting our children to be on their own at an early age, it's time we saw these patterns of parenting behaviour for what they are: survival strategies and adaptations in a culture moving way too fast for intimate relationships. We'll not find the strength to save our planet, save our souls or experience sexual ecstasy by isolation! Our need to attach to others, to depend on them, is perfectly normal and healthy. We remember the touch and security (hopefully) of our mother's body, which we naturally seek again with another.

A great turning point and reckoning in this regard occurs when we first fall in love. Separation anxiety becomes intense as we realise that in bonding and attaching so deeply to another, our bonds to our parents will be forever changed. Our needs to be close, to be protected and to protect, are suddenly transferred to someone new.

Ideally, separation anxiety will motivate us to endure the challenging stages of intimate relationship: marriage, child bearing and rearing, illness and death. It might well be said that strong maternal-infant attachment is really the basis of our ability to meet life's onslaughts with courage and equanimity. If this initial attachment is hindered, whether by social, economic or physiological disruptions, things may predictably go awry. Our subsequent attachments are likely to be inhibited or fractional. The more our ability to relate to others is impaired, the greater our anxiety and dependence. And it is thus that we become targets for emotional abuse.

Even if our original attachments are sound, so vulnerable are we at the time of first love that a whole new configuration of imprints may occur. In his book, *Restoring Innocence*, Alfred Ellis suggests that we can often trace unsatisfying and dysfunctional relationship patterns to our experience of first love. The following questions might serve to illuminate this for you. Did your first love share his/her heart with you or just his/her body? Was he/she patient and kind, or inconsiderate? Was he/she honest and forthright with you, or deceiving and untrue? Did the relationship end amicably or with unresolved anger, pain and humiliation? Did you feel in any way abused by him/her?

This brings us back to the beginning: what, exactly is emotional abuse? It is any behaviour designed to control or subjugate another through emotionally-based techniques of intimidation, ridicule, invalidation, manipulation or verbal assault. Sometimes it's easier to recognise the effects of emotional abuse than the behaviour, particularly for women who have practically become used to being abused. If you are suffering from low self-esteem, lack of trust in your perceptions, inability to appreciate your accomplishments, lack of motivation, chronic depression, or difficulty in taking charge of your life, then you are probably a victim.

In *The Emotionally Abused Woman*, Beverly Engel gives us several typical profiles of abuses. Each of these, she notes, finds a complement in a particular type of abuser. Abusers can be anyone in a role of authority: parents, teachers, bosses, mentors or religious leaders. Or they may be peer counterparts such as siblings, lovers, friends or co-workers.

Interestingly enough, Engel's profiles correspond closely with those women found by Offit to be most prone to sexual difficulty and dysfunction. In any case, it's important to note that these configurations have no inherent progression; one is neither superior nor inferior to another. In fact, women may find themselves moving out of a particular pattern in relationship thinking they are done with it once and for all, only to find themselves playing out yet another abusee role with a new partner. The one thing these roles have in common is that they all align with an experience of powerlessness, self-abnegation or denigration. Frequently, we find ourselves in one pattern or another just as we begin to care deeply for someone; it is precisely at this point that our most basic emotions and fundamental responses are touched and triggered.

Here, then, are five profiles of abusees, composite of Engel's and Offit's observations combined with my own.

### Selfless and Silent

This woman has usually been dominated, controlled or neglected by her parents to such an extreme degree that she has little or no sense of self. She may take on the personality of others, particularly when in love – anything to be accepted. On the other hand, intimacy is both frightening and threatening to her.

When it comes to sex, women in this pattern cycle move in and out of relationships with great frequency. Sex may be either deeply inhibited and unsatisfying or explosive, releasing deep and overwhelming emotions that cannot be integrated. Women stuck in this role are in a turmoil when in love, empty when not. As one of my clients confided to me: 'I don't really know how to be close to a man, but I sure do try. Usually I try to be like him, doing what he likes to do – even in bed, no matter what. Sometimes I feel hurt, sometimes used and very sad, and sometimes this fury rises up in me and I have to get away. I hate that though, because when I'm by myself I don't know who I am. That scares me so much I start looking for someone else right away.'

With this kind of fearful overlay, intimacy of any kind is virtually impossible. As Offit observes, 'In bed, dependence more often leads to erotic extinction than to an eternal

flame of passion.'[3] Women of the silent/selfless temperament are usually attracted to their opposite, highly self-
involved types who have little or no ability to care for
another. The longer a woman stays with a partner like this,
the more she will be drawn into his/her narcissistic,
grandiose schemes. If and when she decides to leave, she
will have to cope with the loss of all she's invested in him/
her, plus a further diminished sense of self.

Women thus afflicted need serious help through hypnosis, long-term psychotherapy or other deep work in
order to trace back patterns of self-abuse to their original
source. It is doubtful that women caught in this role would
even read a book such as this, but if you have a loved one
you are trying to help, encourage her to seek professional
assistance.

## Servile and Compulsive

This role is also excessively dependent, centring around the
expectations of others. Almost every woman in today's
world has some 'pleaser' in her, so deeply ingrained is the
expectation that women should put others' needs before
their own. If taken to an extreme, this type will tolerate and
suffer the demeaning and abusive behaviour of others to an
extent that is utterly damaging to all concerned. Just as she
blames herself for the misdeeds of her intimates, she
likewise impedes them from taking responsibility for their
own actions. If she happens to have a moment of clarity
and notices how others take advantage of her, she will
likely slip into apology for her own behaviour, fully
repressing herself and remaining dependent.

Why does a woman behave thus? Often, her parents
demanded perfection and routinely ignored her personal
boundaries and limitations. She may have been berated

simply for being female (perhaps a son was sorely desired). Whatever the cause, this is a woman unlikely to find happiness in bed. She's far too busy evaluating her performance, assessing it by her partner's standards. 'Was it good enough?' she queries, 'Was I okay, are you *sure* it was really alright?' Unlike the silent/selfless type, she doesn't even have the benefit of occasional explosive release. She is continually in a quandary with regard to her adequacy: preoccupied, distracted from herself, intent on measuring up. By this token, she may avoid sex altogether and focus her obsessive anxiety on her career, or on her children's accomplishments, the cleanliness of her house, etc. In short, she is mortally afraid of losing control, of letting the monster of her own frustrated needs and desires out of the bag.

Characteristically, she does not reach orgasm with intercourse. It goes without saying, I hope, that there are many other reasons for anorgasmia, but as part of the syndrome, a woman in this pattern cannot acknowledge herself fully enough to let go. For her, the 'petite mort' of orgasm is downright terrifying. As Karen related, 'I try to give my lover everything she wants in bed – I give and give until frankly, I feel weak and sick inside. Nothing I do seems to really excite her, and when she finally comes, I start worrying about what she's thinking and whether or not I pleased her. I know I shouldn't say this, but I'd rather put my energy into the house or my work, where I know I can do some good.'

Ironically, this woman is often paired with a controlling type, one who continually reinforces her need to please by being hypercritical.

The servile/compulsive women needs to see that life is not about meeting some outside standard of perfection; it's about personal growth and development. The key here is risk taking, in relatively comfortable but challenging situations. This means doing things strictly for personal pleasure and enrichment: starting from scratch at singing lessons or dance, for example, or trying anything that beckons to one's inner longing. More than any other type, this woman can find happiness by contacting and healing her child self, getting back on her own track in life. Sexually, she needs a new foundation based upon her own needs and desires. And she may need a counsellor's help in identifying the best place to start.

### Guilt-ridden and Reactive

This role is otherwise known as that of the 'sinner'. The woman playing it is more in touch with her desires than the other types I've discussed, but all that her passions bring her is guilt and shame. For the most part, she is so burdened with self-loathing that she can scarcely think about perfection. Women entrenched in this pattern usually have suffered severe physical as well as emotional abuse when young, believing (as they were told) that their naughtiness, seductiveness, or worthlessness was just cause for their violation. As adults, they remain in reaction to these beliefs. Engel puts it most succinctly: 'Sinners believe that bad things only happen to bad people.'[4]

As you might expect, these women pair up with those ready to reinforce their guilt by blaming them for everything under the sun, which only serves to perpetuate their feelings of unworthiness. Blamers are always right; sinners, always wrong. As Sharon revealed, 'My boyfriend says terrible things to me sometimes, and I know I should forgive him but I just can't. Then I see even more how he's right – I really am a terrible person. I don't do the shopping on time because I want to read, or I forget to pay bills because I'm out with my friends.' What about her sex life? 'I'm pretty scared and nervous about sex – I always mess it up. Sometimes I cry and have to stop, I feel so awful inside, and he tells me it's all my fault. He's right, of course, but that just makes it worse. The truth is, I like sex, but I hate what it does to me.'

Reactive women literally absorb their partner's ills and delusions, being sponge-like and compliant. So utterly out of balance do their primary relationships become that often they refer to life and love as nothing but pain – a natural result, really, of such gross disharmony and oppression. Again, deep work to get to the roots of self-deprecation is in order. Often, there's a history of alcoholism or drug abuse in the family.

### Passive and Victimised

Women playing a passive role are targets for victimisation and tragedy. Sexually, these women are apt to be used, are easily manipulated and end up being in the wrong place at the wrong time. The life of the victim is ridden with anxiety; she is extremely vulnerable to the manoeuvres of others. Often, she hooks up with someone who methodically seeks to disempower her by invalidating her actions and perceptions. The more she is invalidated, the greater becomes her passivity and dependency.

Those who become intimately involved with victims are in the explosively dangerous position of having full sway, often to the point of extreme verbal or physical abuse. The victim tells herself she deserves it, that she's inept or just plain crazy. Frequently she has witnessed a similar pattern at home between her father and mother.

Sometimes this woman's partner is something of a sexual sociopath: one who lives for sexual conquest. Offit notes that the sociopath is admired and loved by all – except his (or her) intimates. He deviously and methodically manipulates his partner into submission by never responding to her advances but insisting she respond to his, or by giving her affection only when she's extremely busy so he can then accuse her of not being spontaneous. He may even lead her to question her sanity by pretending never to have said or done things he in fact said or did quite deliberately. He is a master at making others feel uncomfortable while seeming to do nothing at all.[5]

Sex is likely to run just one way: he is always in charge, calling the shots. She will be made to feel ignorant, incomplete, inadequate, and may come to believe that there is something seriously wrong with her body, her technique. As Julie says, 'The only time sex was any good for me was when we were making up – it gave me a chance to express my love to Gene, to reassure myself that he still loved me. The rest of the time I felt too insecure to make any moves in bed, and I don't think Gene wanted me to anyway – I had so many problems. Sometimes, though, I let him force me into it. I suffered through, hoping I could improve myself in his eyes.'

These are the women who report that their partners, 'wonderful men', have told them that their vaginas are too loose, tight, long or short, their orgasms not strong enough, their intensity not quite up to par, their nipples not hard enough, etc., etc. Amazingly, many of these victims are otherwise competent women who either lack experience with sex or have never been particularly in touch with their bodies. Not knowing about themselves makes it easy for them to believe they are deficient, particularly in a culture with role models such as ours.

Passive victims can often be helped by contact with support groups, aided by articulating deep-seated insecurities and feelings of anxiety while overcoming their isolation. Working with women's health, I am saddened by the frequency with which women question the adequacy of their bodies and the appearance of breasts and genitals that are perfectly normal. I find myself time and again telling women during breast examinations that regardless of size, the breasts usually flop apart when a woman lies down, despite cultural premiums on 'stand up tits'. Sometimes a woman will point to her labia and ask if the size, colour or general appearance is okay. It is important to remember that being a victim of sexist conditioning and being an emotional victim in numerous areas of one's life are indeed different by degree.

### Hysterical and Overdrawn

This is the last type we will consider. The word hysterical actually derives from the Latin word for uterus, and common use of the term reflects back to a time when it was believed that an irrational or excitable woman was under the influence of uterine 'ethers' moving about her body. Of late, the term histrionic has come into favour as being less derogatory. I rather like hysterical because it implies a woman under the influence of feminine energies and forces, albeit to an extreme.

At any rate, women thus orientated thrive on intensity, high drama and chaos. Very often, their lives when young were either strictly controlled and inhibited or filled with crisis and disruption. Either way, these women feel most alive and comfortable in the midst of (or while making) a scene. They seek out situations that engender strong emotions like anger or jealousy – anything to stir things up a bit. They frequently choose unstable partners in unstable circumstances. There is a strong tendency continually to upset the balance, to become involved in confrontations that are irreconcilable.

When it comes to love and sex, a woman of this kind will generally choose most unwisely, perhaps a severely anti-social person or an outright mental case. She may be attracted to an alcohol or drug abuser, compulsive gambler, sex addict, or one in trouble with the law. Or she may select the 'hard cases', individuals so disturbed that they are nearly impossible to reach. She may also go for someone unavailable (married, for example) or clearly not inter-ested. She is *not* apt to meet a healthy, somewhat normal person with a decent likelihood of loving her and treating her respectfully.

Ultimately, this woman uses drama as a smoke screen to avoid looking at her own problems and to keep them from getting her attention. Of course, her partner is doing the same; it is the main thing they have in common. The difference is that for the histrionic woman, tension is her drug, and she uses it to keep chaos at a level that feels comfortable. Setting ultimatums, staging rescues, argu-ments and the like, she literally takes on her partner's problems as her own, creating so much stress in the relationship that abuse may come as a welcome release.

Sexually, it's a roller coaster. This woman's counterpart often has a highly changeable and erratic personality ('Dr Jekyll/Mr Hyde', according to Engel) which will of course be intensified by drugs, alcohol or criminal intrigue. Sex can be unbelievably hot and explosive, but at the same time riddled with cruelty and manipulation. The most notice-ably absent quality in both partners is genuine vulner-ability.

Here's a typical report: 'The best thing about our relationship was the sex. I loved trying to entice Jack into sex when he wasn't really in the mood. Sometimes I'd have to make a scene, accuse and argue with him just to get him angry and really hot for me. Then he'd take me to the limit, and I'd scream and holler my way to oblivion. Other times he was cold, cruel and calculating. If I let him make love to me like that, he would trick me out – you know, make it hard for me to come, or make me come at the wrong time. I'd be so angry, I'd pull way back. Then he would apologise, and we'd have blow-out sex again.'

Note the contradictions here; on the one hand, sex was 'the best thing', on the other hand, it was degrading. Clearly, this woman must identify her real need, that of stability and security within herself. Until she can wean herself off the exhilaration that comes from constant crisis, she will be destined for a life of burnout. She must learn to use her need for excitement in constructive ways. Even though not drug or alcohol dependent herself, she may benefit from contact with an abusers' or a family of alcoholics' group, exploring the characteristics of relationship under the shadow of dependency.

If we're truthful with ourselves, we've all played at least one, and probably several, of these roles at some point. Whether abuse is emotional or physical, it all comes down to the same thing: powerlessness, and the need to do something about it. Methods of recovery are many and various, ranging from long-term counselling to self-directed work on the issue. The latter may involve dealing directly or indirectly with both original and current abuser(s), making known all the reasons for anger and hurt, as well as a list of wants and needs from each.

Another cardinal rule: a woman should give herself full permission to do as little or as much work on these issues as feels right. Any woman who has felt forced or compelled into intimate contact against her best interests needs space, and to work always by her own inner clock. If she pushes herself at all, she will sink back into the same familiar patterns of powerlessness. Like so much else about us, work on healing is rhythmic: two steps forward, one step back, rather like delivering a baby. Acknowledging one's limitations is the key to moving beyond them.

## SEXUAL ADDICTION

Let us not confuse sexual addiction with a healthy appetite for intimacy! Some women want and have sex several times a day, especially in the early stages of relationship. And many feel so madly in love in the beginning that they can hardly endure physical separation. This is not an addiction; this is bonding, falling in love.

But when sex is a drug, used to avoid life's difficulties or to seek attention and validation that should really come from ourselves, then there is a problem. It's a fine line: we all use sex for reassurance and to address our most basic needs for touch and intimate contact. But when sexual activity becomes destructive of our work and/or professional relationships, or when it is hurtful to others, sexuality is no longer in its proper life-affirming place.

Consider this case history of a woman caught in negative and compulsive sexual behaviour. Tina reported a tempestuous and stressful phase in a career she actually wanted to escape from; she was overworked and exhausted. She met up with an old friend, now married, and, despite her better judgement, started sleeping with him. In her own words:

> It's not like we were in love. I felt comfortable with him, and it was a release. But the more I did it, the less I felt. I don't know quite how to describe it; it was like I was emotionally dead inside. Still, he took care of me.

Then, of all things, I got pregnant! I haven't been pregnant but once before and this was a total accident, total carelessness. It shocked me into seeing what I was doing. I wasn't taking care of myself at all – just using sex to get by. I had an abortion and ended the relationship.

Here, an otherwise assertive and successful woman became a passive victim in an intimate relationship. The stress, the uncertainty, the inability to face the changes impending in her life led to some very self-destructive and painful behaviour.

Another example from Janelle, married with a child:

My husband was the classic executive, straight-arrow, in his head all the time, tense and anxious. After our son was born, sex just stopped. I felt like I had dried up inside, that I was losing my beauty and my charm. I started an affair with a man in the neighbourhood – he was unemployed and his wife worked – I even knew her slightly. He had problems, and I tried to help. It was so wonderful to be needed, to be admired, to have that hot kind of sex that is just so good! But after a while I started seeing him for what he was – a troubled man, a loser, really, and somebody else's husband. Quite suddenly I saw how I'd been using him to avoid the disappointment I felt in my own marriage, and my anxieties about getting a life of my own. It was a rude awakening to things I'd been putting off for a long time.

Examples like this abound. But then, there is sexual addiction that involves the apparently insatiable appetite, bringing to mind nymphomania. Is there really such a condition per se, or is it merely a symptom of other emotional or psychological problems? Probably the latter, at least by today's standards. Most sexologists see the condition as resulting from a lack of healthy attachment and separation experiences. Nymphomaniacs can't bear to be alone; they crave to a nearly manic extent the comforts of human contact, presumably to make up for some deprivation when young.

Most of us have known or heard of women like these, in bed with a new man almost every night, always 'on the make'. They have so much basic anxiety that intercourse, no matter how frequent, doesn't make so much as a dent in their insecurity.

Some are multi-orgasmic and may climax as many as 20 or more times in one sexual experience, able to stop only when totally exhausted. Others report orgasms to be unfulfilling and monotonous. The great majority are rarely orgasmic. The uncontrollable aspect of their behaviour causes so much stress that it is impossible to relax and release. In short, women in this pattern are profoundly immature, very deeply injured and repressed from years before.

There is another behavioural possibility when history of sexual, emotional or psychological abuse is at issue. That is to forego sex altogether for a time until the ground is set for new and healthier patterns of intimacy. In the next chapter, we will look at abstinence as an increasingly common choice for women trying to rid themselves of destructive sexual behaviour. There are a number of other reasons why women take up celibacy, too, as we are about to see.

1. Davis, Laura; and Bass, Ellen, *The Courage to Heal* (New York, Harper & Row, 1988)
2. Kitzinger, Sheila, *Women's Experience of Sex* (New York, Penguin Books, 1985)
3. Offit, Avodah K., *The Sexual Self* (New York, J.B. Lippincott, 1977)
4. Engel, Beverly, *The Emotionally Abused Woman* (Los Angeles, Lowell House, 1990)
5. Offit, *The Sexual Self*

# 8

# Sexual abstinence
# and celibacy

The woman who decides, for whatever reason, that she wishes to abstain from sex has been looked upon by our society as something of a anomaly. Sexual activity so deeply pervades our cultural definition of happiness and fulfilment that a woman going without is automatically presumed to be deprived and longing. As will be shown in the following pages, nothing could be further from the truth, at least when abstinence is a choice.

In fact, more and more women are deciding to take time off from sexual activity when preoccupied with personal issues and problems. Social autonomy has set the stage for women's emotional self-determination. The cultural constraints of the 1950s that defined sex for women as either taboo or obligatory no longer hold sway. Women may be categorically portrayed in the media as sex objects, but they are increasingly shown to have sexual identities and lives of their own. That a woman would, under circumstances of stress or emotional strain, decide it best to keep her vital energies to herself is certainly understandable.

To illustrate, here is a story of my own experience some years ago. My husband and I were going through a particularly difficult time in our relationship; we were not yet married (a bone of contention between us) and were working out negative consequences of an affair he'd had some time earlier. That these issues were disrupting our sex life was quite natural, to my thinking, although I won't deny I was concerned. Our therapist, who had additional training in sex therapy, showed us a tape one day of a couple engaged in foreplay, according to specific recommendations and step-by-step instructions. This experience both mortified and frustrated me, and I told her outright, 'I don't *need* this, I don't think we have any problems with technique. My problem is with my feelings, my pain and vulnerability, the trust issue. I think if we work on these, our sex life will be fine.' This is not to minimise sex therapy for those with unusual aversions or physical difficulties, but for the vast majority of women, sexual dysfunction is emotionally based, and nothing more. We don't need another survey to tell us that a woman cannot be loving, open and orgasmic if she feels her partner is treating her poorly or unfairly, let along if she can't do right by herself.

What is it like to take a sexual time-out? It depends on the situation, but most women report a typical progression from loneliness to self-confidence and clarity. Brenda, a single, career-orientated woman in her thirties, tells how a series of relationships frightened her into abstinence that then became voluntary for a period of seven months.

I had an outrageous affair with a fellow who turned out to be royalty, a Scottish lord in fact. It was a whirlwind romance – in a matter of weeks he proposed marriage. On the one hand, I knew I'd be 'taken care of' for life, and all my friends were telling me to go for it. But this is a pattern that keeps re-occurring in my life – guys go crazy for me, and the situation becomes overwhelming. Maybe I have something to do with it – after all, I let it happen, to a point. Then I feel this pressure of being swept away, and I notice that it happens more when I'm unsettled or stressed at work.

So, I said no to this guy with *much* relief, and then the same thing happened with a man who turned out to be married – there were signs and signals that I never followed up until it was way too late. After this I pulled back completely from men and sex.

Being celibate for all these months has given me some important things. One is protection – I can feel vulnerable with myself and not be at risk. Another is a very clear picture of what I want in relationship: marriage to the right man. Eventually, because now I'm content to wait.

Other comments from women in similar circumstances: 'I'm pleased and proud to be nurturing me'; 'I see the seeds of myself beginning to grow'; 'I have inner conviction now – I'm my own person'. It would seem, in a way, that voluntary abstinence is something of a right of passage for women today, particularly in reaction to tremendously eased sexual mores.

Yet another factor in the upsurge of celibacy is women's alienation from the monthly cycle, particularly the menstrual phase. No one explains in more detail the time honoured and cross cultural significance of menstrual taboos than Esther Harding in her book, *Women's Mysteries*. Women have ostensibly been isolated during menstruation in the belief that their presence, gaze or touch would cause contamination. But in truth, women's natural contact with their innermost selves, their highly personal yet extraordinarily universal awareness at this time, threatens to undermine (and may likewise transform) business as usual for the rest of society. Women have been isolated for yet another reason; their sexual energies are overwhelmingly magnetic. Taboos have dictated this regular period of sexual solitude for women each month, a cyclical phase of abstinence wherein self-examination and spiritual renewal (alone or in the company of others who are menstruating) were anticipated and encouraged. A basic need for such a respite – to be able to have one's body and soul to oneself periodically without guilt or anxiety – may be at the root of many problems in relationships that result in the decision to forego sex completely.

Let us examine this premise by way of example, taking first that of Lynda, who explains:

> I grew up in a household where mum's main task was taking care of everyone else's business. I loved her for it, hated her for it, learned to depend on her and not myself. Even though we fought bitterly when I was in my teens, I found myself continually dependent and wanting to please her before myself, even as an adult. Three marriages and three children later, I still don't know all that much about me. My sexuality has been restrained, I think, confined to what's expected. I've been abstinent for three months now, and it's been a good way for me to sort things out and get to the heart of who I am. To tell you the truth, I feel like a child now, discovering broken threads from the past and reweaving them. Right now, I don't want anyone else but me.

This points to a primary need of women throughout time, that of self-containment. *Women and Madness*, by Phyllis

Chester, explores the consequence of diffusing the self for the ease and pleasure of others until complete disintegration of personality threatens to occur. When a woman rallies from this position it is usually with passion and fury; a passion that requires no other partner than herself.

Sometimes sexual excess leads to celibacy. This too is a classic theme, and women are not exempt. Here is what Alena has to say:

> I was rather repressed when I was young, living in a house that was immaculately clean and bound by strict rules of behaviour. There was love, but there was also fear; my mum was afraid of herself, I guess. I took the road less travelled (at least in my family) and dropped out of school. I met wild and wonderful people, and found I could make good money selling sexual favours. Not prostitution exactly, but intimate massages, blow jobs, that kind of thing. I was choosy, though, and never a slave to anyone. For a while I felt free, for the first time in my life. Then good friends turned bad, a few died of drug overdoses, and I turned to religion. I needed to purify myself, and I didn't have sex with anyone for three years.

As we enter our second decade of confronting HIV and Aids, stories like this become increasingly rare. Nevertheless, sexual addiction and overindulgence remain major pathways to celibacy for a number of women.

More commonly, women complain of feeling prostituted in seemingly conventional relationships. Often this comes from denying the pain of fundamental needs going unmet, being ignored or belittled. The resulting sexual pattern may be rather sporadic; a few sexual encounters over a period of a day or two (perhaps after an argument) and then weeks with no contact. Recent research has shown that sporadic sexual activity is more likely to cause menstrual irregularity and sub-fertility than is celibacy. (Orgasm via masturbation does not seem to compensate.) Either regular sex, or none at all, tends to maintain normal hormonal levels and rhythms.[1]

Nothing disrupts sexual closeness like infidelity. Trust is so basic to a healthy relationship that once it is violated, intimacy may be nearly impossible to regain without a break or time alone to heal. Again, a classic account from Harriet:

> My husband was unfaithful from day one, but it took me years to acknowledge it. Once I did, I went crazy with jealousy and fear. I started having anxiety attacks, even in public places. I'd just be going along fine, when suddenly I'd feel breathless, lightheaded, my heart would be racing and I'd have to sit down. I ended my marriage, but the same thing happened with the next guy. I finally realised that sex had become so full of fear and pain for me that I would probably keep losing again and again, unless I broke the cycle on my own. So I quit looking for validation from men, for breathtaking romance, and got down to being by myself. Somedays I felt so alone that panic and anxiety nearly got me, but eventually, I could catch these feelings right away and set myself free. I discovered the things that nourished me and made me feel complete, instead of trying to be like somebody else.

Probably the most important lesson women on the rebound must learn is that the basic natures of both men and women, whether biologically or culturally programmed, are definitely different. According to the research presented in *Brain Sex*, there is overwhelming evidence that men are by nature polygamous and tend to focus on sex for its own sake.[2] This does not preclude romance or even monogamous commitment, but a woman needs to know what she is up against. In any case, happiness comes not from seeking your own version of perfection but by accepting men for what they are, then hopefully finding one so compatible and desirous of involvement that the two of you have at least a fighting chance. Relationships involve conflict because male and female natures are at odds, but they can also be viewed as complementary. Each has certain basic needs that are fairly consistent; John Gray has illuminated this quite well. For example, women need to feel cared for and loved in order to be able to trust their partners. Men, on the other hand, need to be trusted in order to give; a man without a woman's trust loses his momentum, his vitality. Naturally, men will fail to care for women as women would like, and women will find reason to lose trust in men, but that doesn't change the basic needs of each. The more realistic we are about differences between the sexes, and the more we accept our own traits and tendencies, the better we will be at weathering the natural phases in relationships, the inevitable challenges and disappointments.

Beyond sexual stereotyping, when a woman chooses sexual abstinence, for a time she has the opportunity to own both her masculine and feminine aspects and to bring them to terms with one another. For example, she can look at how much love and nourishment she gives to herself, and, if minimal, at the resulting lack of trust and vulnerability she feels with others. This will not change her basic needs once she is in relationship: no matter how well she has learned to care for herself, she will still be vulnerable to a lack of caring from her partner. However, she may be better equipped to deal with breakdowns in communication and estrangement when they occur and go on caring for herself regardless.

How positive or constructive a period of abstinence is for a woman largely depends on how deliberate it is. When abstinence is by choice, negative side effects such as depression, lack of motivation, or uninterest in personal upkeep may not occur. It is important to note that just as it may benefit a woman to be free of too much concern about her appearance, it can also affect her negatively if she doesn't keep herself up. However, if she lets everything go for a while, she may then feel free to find a new style that suits her.

More than occasional depression demands attention and some revision of priorities, as do feelings of boredom or being stuck and stagnant. Women's groups can help tremendously with this process, and need not be all that formal. You can start a women's circle by meeting regularly with others so inclined. You can make your time together whatever you want, involving ritual and choosing topics for discussion such as money, sexuality, jealousy, or whatever feels most relevant at the time. In my experience, great revelations can occur in such groups without any professional assistance. Another possibility is to choose a book or text, for example one on women's mysteries or meditations, and work through it together.

Since women do not find much cultural affirmation for abstinence, they really need the support of one another. Remember that for men, sex is a prerequisite for emotional release, a precursor to love. Women, on the other hand, are readily able to love themselves and others without sexual demonstration. Women who choose celibacy are threatening to men because their choice is irreconcilable with male needs; we see this reflected in our language by terminology that is far from flattering, such as old maid, spinster, and prude. In the days of witch burnings, it is notable that the vast majority of victims were single women of advanced age, so unacceptable was it for women to refuse to be vessels for male satisfaction and procreation.[3] On the other hand, women worry about needing sexual contact to remain physically youthful and attractive, as if going without sex might cause them to shrivel up and die! Certainly masturbation can serve to relieve tension, stimulate pelvic circulation and provide pleasure. And there are many other ways to find physical, emotional and spiritual satisfaction and release. Some women just don't like sex, for whatever reason, and that's all there is to it. The bottom line is that women are more sexually independent than men, precisely because they are better able to recognise and meet their needs themselves.

What, if any, are the physical effects of long-term abstinence? Again, with so many motivating factors, it is difficult to generalise. Some women do report symptoms of pelvic tension such as chronic backache, increased premenstrual tension or menstrual difficulties, but just as many report cessation of the above, particularly when abstinence is the result of a stressful or painful intimate relationship. Oddly enough, many women report losing touch somewhat with their monthly cycle, being less aware of fertile signs and premenstrual signals. Particularly if fertility awareness has been used for contraceptive purposes, this is understandable. But I wonder if these women are really so out of touch with their cycles on an emotional or physic level. A considerable number report that abstinence clears the way for better alignment with their feelings and psychological needs by simplifying the dynamics, so to speak.

Many women notice increased awareness of diet and

health when on their own. Without the distraction of another's needs, they are better able to see the results of their own eating and lifestyle habits, and to experiment with what makes them feel best. Particularly if a woman has been living with someone and cooking and eating more to suit his/her wishes than her own, she may find this aspect of being alone most illuminating and beneficial.

Women often say that the less sex they have, the less they think about it. Sometimes the longing for contact is strong, but usually it's more a desire for intimacy than sex itself (unless a woman is peak-fertile or premenstrual). Being celibate is less about not having sex than it is about being alone, dealing with one's own body, psyche and soul. The periodic desire for intimacy is part of the deal, and should be seen as a personal manifestation of need rather than the result of having someone attractive around.

Other reasons why a woman might choose to avoid having sex temporarily have little to do with relationships. For example, a woman friend of mine recently shared plans for a year long trip around the world, and decided to forego sexual involvement until she left. No dates, no serious flirting, just packing and settling affairs. Similar indications might indicate plans to move house, to change careers or focus on a creative project. As a spiritual discipline, celibacy has long been reputed to enhance one's concentration if undertaken with clear and serious resolve: something to think about and keep open as an option.

And what if a woman elects to take this option in spite of the fact that she is married or in intimate partnership? We read and hear much about differences in sexual desire between partners and, at last, the periodic desire for abstinence is coming out of the closet. This affects both men and women (though the former less intensely). When considering national surveys on the frequency of sex in relationships, we must remember that they deal in averages. And in these will certainly figure less than desired episodes, unsatisfactory contacts, as well as the flurry of sexual activity common in the initial stages of a relationship when major challenges to intimacy have yet to be faced. I can think of no long-term study that reflects the phases of closeness and separation in enduring relationships.

How *does* a couple get by when one wants sex and the other does not? Ideally they discuss the matter and set themselves limits. If emotional issues arise or become acute, they may decide they need outside help. Marriages in distress are frequently challenged to redefine sex from an obligatory or perfunctory activity to one of free will. Periods of abstinence may be crucial to sorting out individual needs and concerns. If either partner has been unfaithful, physically abusive or psychologically brutal to the other, so much more case. After all, what possible tenderness, joy or security could come from sexual contact under such trying circumstances?

Personal trauma of any kind is likely to interfere with a couple's sex life, particularly the loss of a loved one. The death of a child, a parent, a dear friend or relative may cause either a desperate need for contact or else complete disinterest. If only one partner is affected, the other may provide stable ground. But if both are devastated, as by the loss of a child, getting into the emotional intensity of sex may be just too much to handle. Rhythms of processing grief may also be at odds so that when one partner is raw and vulnerable, the other is shut down and unable to feel much of anything. Here is Amanda's story of what happened to her after the death of her son at eight weeks from SIDS (Sudden Infant Death Syndrome – Cot Death):

I don't think there is anything more horribly painful on earth than losing a child, at least, I hope there's not, because I don't think I could endure it. Jerry and I had many sad and upsetting experiences trying to make love after Jason's death, but this one time was so amazing I must share it with you. We were fucking and crying, really, fucking and crying, when we felt something descend on us, a great break in the tension, a feeling of warmth and healing. It was so wonderful, I can't tell you – a perfect state of grace. Sex aside, orgasms aside, in that moment, time stood still and we felt whole again. After this, we stopped doubting and blaming ourselves so much. The guilt began to lift, and we began to live life again.

Re-establishing intimacy after any kind of intensely painful experience or shock is a difficult process; this couple was lucky to find common ground. Time heals, more than anything else. Realigning oneself after deep trauma is hardly a simple matter; layer upon layer must be permeated with new hope, definition and resolve. For a time, we strongly encouraged people to express their grief profoundly and immediately; we now see that mourning and grieving are in fact cyclic processes and may take years and years to complete. The same is true, by the way, for anyone recovering from experiences of physical, emotional and/or sexual abuse. Tina relates: 'Pat and I had known each other for about a year, while she was still living with her previous partner. Then she and I became intimate, and she decided to leave Sue. She felt great guilt about this decision, along with new sadness and confusion regarding patterns of passivity from childhood abuse. Just as she became free to be with me, she decided she couldn't be sexual for a while. That was okay; I understood.'

Coping with the effects of debilitating illness, handicap or mutilating surgery such as mastectomy or hysterectomy can also call for a sexual time off.

Sometimes, the desire for abstinence becomes permanent, as in Joan's case:

I'm 69 now, and my husband died six years ago. A couple of years after his death, friends tried to set me up with men, and at first I was curious, interested. But each time it was so obviously wrong that all I felt was revulsion. I'd think to myself, 'I have to get in bed with *that*?' I had such a wonderful marriage, and now I have my children and grandchildren. I've got used to being alone, and honestly, I like it.

At the other end of spectrum we have the plain, old-fashioned desire to wait for the right relationship. More and more women are choosing to remain virgins late into their teens or throughout their early twenties, no longer feeling so intense a pressure to prove their sexual liberation. Less and less are women expected to sleep around. This has much to do with living in the shadow of AIDS and other sexually transmitted diseases.

Thus, for the first time in modern history, women are discovering the freedom to choose from a spectrum of sexual options. And now that sex by coercion is being defined as abuse, women have an opportunity to explore themselves as sexual beings in non-sexual phases. The ultimate dictum of sexual therapy – 'Don't worry about pleasing your partner, start by pleasing yourself' – may soon be realised by women on a mass scale. In the process, women will see that their sexual energy is vital to their own well-being and instrumental to creativity, health and happiness, whether shared with another or not. Indeed, it will seem increasingly natural and acceptable that a woman (or man) should have phases when sexual interaction is either inappropriate, undesirable or low on the list of priorities, and that there will be times when sexual energy is channelled into highly personal pursuits.

1.   Cutler, Winnifred, *Love Cycles* (New York, Villard Books, 1991)
2.   Moir, A., Jessel, D., *Brain Sex* (New York, Carol Publishing Co., 1991)
3.   Walker, Barbara, *The Crone* (San Francisco, Harper & Row, 1985)

# 9

# Your own patterns

How you make use of the material in this book depends on many things, not the least of which are any unresolved issues of abuse, grief or loss. These so strongly affect your receptivity and sense of self that they certainly overshadow natural changes at different stages of life.

And yet, as we live each day and notice the turning of each cycle, we also begin to observe certain things about ourselves, ways in which we remain troubled or inhibited: our toughest challenges. The more creatively and constructively we are able to work on these, the richer and more multi-dimensional our experience at the next stage will be.

This closing chapter is written workbook style, with specific questions intended to shed light on these psychosexual patterns. Rather than allow blank space for writing within the book, I encourage you to use separate paper. The questions are provocative and intimately revealing, and I doubt you'd want someone browsing through your bookshelves to come across your responses.

But *do* write your answers down! Committing yourself

in writing is altogether different from musing, even if aloud. As you write, you may notice certain words that keep cropping up, or phrases from the treasure box of your past that have deep and vivid meaning for you. Or you may find empty expressions that you might wish to rethink or change.

If you'd like to evoke your personal sentiments more strongly, you might choose a coloured pen that best represents your mood during a particular period and write with it. Or design a symbol – an open circle, a square cut in half, whatever – that summarizes your feelings at a certain stage, and place it at the top of each appropriate page. Your symbol can certainly change during a given cycle; you may well find that it does. If you have a tarot deck, select a card at critical junctures that embodies your feelings and beliefs, and make note of it. You may also change your name as you write, to a nickname or private 'soul' name that no one knows but you.

The journey through the labyrinth of sexuality is not only personal, it is mythic, too. Don't be afraid to lend this dimension of value and significance to the intimate details of your life.

### DISCOVERING YOUR CYCLE

If you are just now learning about your monthly cycle, certain questions and concerns will probably arise. Most women wonder why no one ever told them these facts about sex and their bodies before. Do you feel angry at having been kept in the dark this way? Or do you feel foolish or inept at never having noticed cyclic changes yourself? Does your formerly tranquil mind now reel with paranoia of plots and conspiracies against women in general? Or do you simply feel loss and sadness at having missed out on this aspect of yourself for some period of time? Quite commonly, women are both disturbed and exhilarated to think that romantic feelings attributed to a particular relationship or partner were in large part biological promptings coming from their own bodies at certain times of the month.

You may wish to go back through the questions in the previous paragraph and examine your feelings more closely. Explore them a bit in writing. See if you can get in touch with your history here, tracing back attitudes, inhibitions and expectations. Go back to the beginning: how did you learn about menstruation? What was your menarche like – was it hidden away from the rest of your family and friends, or acknowledged in some positive way? And how did you learn about sex? Were you given a chance to question? What were your initial explorations like? Do you remember the first time you masturbated? How was it having sex the first time? How did you feel afterwards? Balance the downside of any of these events by recalling the moments of power when you really felt good about yourself. Evoke the curious, courageous you, unfettered by guilt or fear, confidently following your destiny, and see this aspect apart from all the shoulds and shouln'ts you bear.

Choose this, or another image of yourself, and bring it to the task at hand: discovering and trusting your cycle. If you are troubled with PMS, irregular menses or infertility with no apparent physical cause, ask your wise self for counsel. Do this in writing, song, meditation or dreams.

If you feel completely out of touch, can't remember anything or can't deal with this at all, refer to Chapter Seven particularly the checklist on sexual abuse.

If your cycle is basically smooth and trouble free, take a moment to consider why. Do you follow any particular menstrual routine or ritual? Cultural mores see menstrual blood on a spectrum from dirty to sacred. How do you feel about it? Do you enjoy and make the most of your fertile time? How so? How do you benefit most from paying attention to your cycle? And what do you have yet to learn about honouring your rhythms?

If you are at the point of completing this sort of personal investigation, single out whatever aspects remain troublesome or unsettled for you. These are your carry-over issues. As you move through other stages, you will come to see these problems in a different context, which may enable you to solve them.

### PREGNANT FOR THE FIRST TIME

Having your first baby? Then you have much to contemplate, many emotional changes to enlighten and frighten you. You may have already discovered by now that pregnancy is definitely a social event. You are probably being bombarded with questions, advice, even physical contact (belly touching) from absolute strangers. This, you can't avoid. In fact, if you can stay somewhat open and objective, you may see in those encounters that affect you most deeply some fundamental bit of your conditioning that has been triggered.

Let's look at the background once again. What did your mother tell you about birth? How did you react? What about your grandmother, great-grandmother or other female relatives? Try to recollect your *feelings* at these moments of revelation. Apart from any messages of fear or humiliation, if you were to summon each of these women now to stand before you, what sort of wisdom might each impart as to how to cope with labour?

Control is such an issue in pregnancy and birth. How do

you personally feel about losing control? About feeling and appearing vulnerable? What do you think you might do if the pain really got to you? What sorts of things might your partner and midwife or doctor do to help you feel better? What might you do to help yourself? Do any of these relate to your sensual/sexual likes and dislikes?

Look at the last few questions, and see if there are things you might teach your partner and/or midwife now. For example, maybe you love to have your hair stroked, or your head held, only nobody knows but you. Pregnancy is the time to make these desires known – absolutely.

Fantasise about yourself in labour. Where are you? Is it dark, light, noisy or quiet? Who is with you, and what are they doing? What are you doing? What position are you in, how are you breathing, and how do you feel?

Now imagine labour suddenly getting much stronger. Wow – it really hurts! How do you react? Do you expand, or contract? Do you reach out, or close yourself off? Relate this response to your experience with sex. What do you do when it stops feeling good, either emotionally, or physically? Sometimes, women think they want to have sex even as they find themselves totally shutting down. Think about the times this has happened to you. Was it really sex you wanted, or something else? Crack the code on this, and you'll discover the kind of support you're most likely to need in labour.

When you do feel sexually frustrated, how do you handle it? Do you ask for what you want, get angry, sulk, or just withdraw? In every possible area of your life, especially in bed, practise asking for what you need, when you need it. This is core preparation for giving birth.

A little something more: how do you respond when others try to tell you what's good for you? Do you clam up, concede to keep the peace, become angry, or assert your position? When it comes to extraneous advice during labour or routine procedures you do not want, how would you like to respond? What do you think would be most effective?

## PREGNANT AGAIN?

Whether carrying your second, third or fourth baby, you will probably have issues remaining from your other birth experiences that merit attention. The central question is this: did you feel in any way violated during your birth experience? Were things done to you or the baby that you did not desire or without your permission? Was your privacy invaded? Did you feel powerless, unsupported, ridiculed or ridiculous in a way you can't let go of? Were promises broken by your doctor or midwife? Do you feel they abandoned you during or after the birth?

If any of the above fit, you may want to write a letter to the appropriate parties. Whether you send it or not, the writing is therapeutic. You may not want to send the first draft, but may decide to send the second. I personally think it is critical to let your doctor or midwife know how you feel – critical for you, for them, and for other women they serve.

How about your partner? Did he/she let you down, or disappoint you in any way? Do you have feelings about what happened during labour that you never shared? Did the birth affect your sex life/intimacy? Again, a letter is a good place to start; it can help you get your thoughts and feelings in order before you begin to discuss them.

If your partner's behaviour during the birth relates to some pre-existing problem that the two of you have already discussed many times, you may be ripe for outside intervention via counselling. Perhaps you see the need, but can you assert it? If not, you yourself may be bound by some strong feelings of personal unworthiness. Perhaps you have a history of abuse. You need to find support and the opportunity to express your anxiety, either one to one with a counsellor or in group therapy.

Do this work now; read and educate yourself on the option for giving birth, communicate your hopes and desires, and your next experience could be fundamentally different – the birth of your dreams!

## NEWLY POSTPARTUM

If you are newly (or recently) postpartum, you may be encountering feelings of dependency. Often these arise during labour, although you may not have recognised them as such. Feelings of dependency are strongly linked to a fear of abandonment.

Let us not confuse dependency with vulnerability. Vulnerability is quite normal in labour, and is actually a desired state. It is characterised by high levels of sensitivity, openness and receptivity. Dependency, in contrast, is marked by feelings of not being able to rely on oneself, of needing others to define one's reality.

Actually, hospital policies and personnel often engender feelings of dependency in patients so that they will be compliant, even with the use of highly invasive, unnecessary procedures. But once a woman's power has thus been unsurped, she may become desperately afraid that whoever has taken it will leave her behind and abandon her to the worst.

Here are some questions to help you see where you stand on this. Do you generally find it hard to focus on your own needs? Do you often feel that everyone else has power but you? Do you experience anxiety attacks when people pull away or reject you? These are actually behavioural characteristics of women who have suffered abuse, whether birth related or not. They also correlate to a family background of drug or alcohol dependency.

There is yet another category of abuse to consider: that perpetrated by society. In Chapter Four, we looked at the routine abandonment of new mothers in the United States. Even women who have led relatively stable lives may find themselves exhibiting typical dependency/fear of abandonment symptoms: anxiety and depression.

Women can pull themselves out of this only with the support of truly sympathetic family members or other women. Generally, the solution is as much a matter of practical assistance with recovery and household responsibilities as it is emotional support.

But other women are hard pressed to tolerate even the basic vulnerability of motherhood. Long before the birth, did you resolve that having a baby would disrupt your life as little as possible? Perhaps you chose to have medication very early in labour – sometimes there is a correlation here. Fear of motherhood can often be traced back to rigid sex-role division of labour and limited love and affection in one's family. Was your other long-suffering, with a decidedly negative view of menstruation, child bearing and sexuality? If you are deeply uncomfortable about caring for your baby, frustration can build up and in extreme cases can lead to violence. Get help. Make an anonymous call to a women's switchboard, talkline or counselling referral service.

We've discussed the typical sexual frustrations postpartum. Are you compounding these with negative feelings about your body? Do you find your copious secretions (milk, lochia, sweat) offensive? Do you feel ashamed that you look a bit softer or plumper than usual? Or can you take pride in your body for all it has accomplished, birth and breastfeeding and day-to-day recovery, along with care of the newborn baby?

Has your weight been an issue for most of your adult life? If so, you'll probably be somewhat unhappy post-partum. Have you a history of eating disorders? Nothing is worse than trying to diet while breastfeeding; in fact, you need more calories than you did while pregnant. Exercise is the answer, even though it takes a while to get used to going out with the baby in a sling, or to find the energy and time to do an exercise video while the baby naps.

Other considerations: do you feel conflict between being a mother and being sexual? Where does this come from? What are your partner's attitudes on this subject? It may seem awkward to switch back and forth between erotic and maternal feelings as abruptly as you do at this stage, but eventually they will find their place in your life.

What it all comes down to is this: can you give yourself permission to change and grow? Your body is changing – can you trust it to tell you what to eat and drink, trust that it will fully recover in good time, trust that its promptings for rest are to be heeded? Or do you feel, on the other hand, that your body has somehow betrayed you? Have others told you outright that your body is not up to par, not good enough? Think of every individual who has told you this throughout the years, and explore your respective feelings. Can you let go of your anger and find forgiveness?

Keep a journal of your daily accomplishments at this stage, noting in particular every way in which your body works for you. Pay special attention to the times you feel physically well and wonderful, and write them down.

## JUGGLING CAREER, FAMILY AND INTIMACY

The work to be done in this area can probably be summed up in a single question: what are your priorities? Often, we learn more about our values if we examine the priorities of our parents. Are we emulating them, reacting against what they believe, or truly on our own?

Ever since the 1950s, women have typically attempted to do too much. How was it in your household? What were the messages you got from your mother regarding house-work? Responsibility for children? Responsibility for emotional issues? Responsibility for individual health and well-being?

What was your mother's attitude regarding her privacy? Did she take private time? What were the things she loved to do – just for herself? Did she set boundaries that you and other family members were aware of and respected?

Generally, women tend to make care of their children a top priority, and that is as it should be. But, did your mother have any help? What kind and how often? Do you think it was enough?

This brings us to the subjects of stress and anger. How did she handle each of these? How do you handle each of these? And how does what you do, or don't do, affect you and your loved ones?

What was your parents' attitude about their intimate relationship? Did they let their romantic feelings for one another show? Did they make time for their love, apart from you? How open were your parents about sexual matters? What sort of charge did the subject of sex carry in your household? By the same token, were your personal boundaries and need for privacy respected by your family?

Take a look at your current weekly workload. You may benefit from writing down all that you do, then calculating the amount of time spent in each general area: career, housework, family interaction, personal pursuits and private time with your partner. Play with this on paper, look at any gross imbalance and re-allocate your time according to what you really want. Many of us believe we are trapped in unsatisfactory lifestyle patterns by necessity, when in fact these are a matter of habit. What every woman in this stage of life needs to recognise is that there will *never* be enough time to do and have it all. Instead, the source of self-satisfaction can change from week to week and month to month, depending on any urgent needs. Dial and tune your reality, and resolve to stop being a victim.

If this seems extremely difficult for you, look back at your family history, and your responses to the questions in previous sections of this chapter. What are the patterns? Perhaps if you can see where and when you give up your power, you will be able to figure out why.

## PASSING THROUGH MENOPAUSE

As was mentioned in Chapter Six, your responses in this phase are likely to reflect those of female relatives and particularly your mother. What did she experience at menopause? Is there anything of her experience that you personally remember? Since most women tend to hide these changes, you may want to ask her about any erratic behaviour you recall and see what the two of you can piece together.

Moving to yet another area: how do you feel about the passing of youth? Or do you believe that youth is merely a state of mind, one that can be maintained indefinitely? If so, what are you doing to keep yourself young and vital? Are you keeping up with your interests? How about your spiritual life?

And how are you caring for your body at this point? Take inventory of all current measures you are taking to try to stay physically youthful and attractive. Truthfully, are any of these a waste of time and money? What does seem to work for you, and can you place greater priority on it?

Have you talked to your partner about your fears and anxieties at this point in your life? Has she/he been supportive? As the hormonal surges of menopause move you deeper and closer to your deepest concerns and longings, do you find yourself able to utilise these visions? Are you incorporating them into your life or merely coping?

Begin to think about where you want to go with the energy of 'the change'. Use it as a springboard to shift and expand your lifestyle. Where do you find courage in general, and where can you find it most right now?


## GROWING OLDER AND WISER

How do you feel about growing older? What do you still look forward to doing and accomplishing? And how about your partner? Have you discussed your rounding-out goals and dreams with one another?

What, if any, are the lessons you have yet to learn in life? About the situations that keep repeating themselves? And what will it take for you to move through them? Can you deliberately set the stage? To what degree are you willing to do this? In terms of these, your toughest challenges, what is your source of strength for confronting them, and how do you get to that source?

With regard to sex itself: how is your communication with your partner? Are you happy with yourself sexually? More or less than before? In terms of sexual expression, are there things you'd still like to try and do? How do you think your partner would feel if you did so?

Look closely, and look back. What, if any, are the ways you still don't feel comfortable with your body? The parts you never learned to love? The sexual wounds and/or criticisms you've never healed? See if you can find a way to embrace yourself fully, and truly incorporate every part. In terms of longevity, a healthy body is an integrated body.

How are your relationships with your grown-up children? Are you comfortable sharing ideas with them, or do you feel like a nag? Identify your crone/destroyer aspect: wise, objective and irrevocably frank. When the crone speaks, she does so from a point of clarity and certitude. Feel the difference in tone between whining/cajoling and speaking the truth, unfettered by expectation.

Do you have other outlets for your accumulated wisdom? Can you find any more? Your vitality is strongly linked to this fundamental sort of self-expression.

Have you considered taking the role of family historian? Perhaps, if you have not done so already, you might begin to assemble and organise papers and photographs into albums, adding your own narrative if you like. Each of your children may have his or her own album, and there may be a more general one that includes the family tree. These will be treasured by your offspring, and will put much into perspective for you while bringing to a close certain periods of your life.

## IN SUMMARY

Now that you've had a chance to work on each phase of life you've already experienced, and have read about others yet to come, perhaps you have begun to see some underlying themes of family history, cultural conditioning, self-discovery and ultimately, transcendence. For beyond self-realisation and integration, the transcendental aspect of sexual expression is what keeps us coming back for more. As Andrew Weil has pointed out in his book, *The Natural Mind*, the desire for altered states of reality is with us from the time we are very young: why else do children spin wildly in circles until they fall down dizzy and laughing, only to get up and do it again? It becomes a bit more difficult to find appropriate ways to do this as we mature, but that doesn't mean we shouldn't go on trying!

As women, our journey through this particular period of history is tremendously rich and complex. Having an overview of the cycles and stages in life can help us keep our wits about us, retain our sense of humour and become wise. Even now, the men's movement is becoming better defined, and likewise seeks a complete view of what it means to be male: personally, interpersonally and socially. Never has it been more important, or in many ways easier, to articulate all that it means to be female.

Nevertheless, way too many women live in poverty, in abusive situations or other conditions of hardship for us to become complacent. We have so much to do, so much to speak and write about, so much to share across the generations. May our sexual vitality and sensitivity infuse these tasks with passion, commitment and love. And may we readily find courage at every crossroads.

# Index

All Optima books are available at your bookshop or
newsagent, or can be ordered from the following address:
  Little, Brown and Company (UK) Limited,
  P.O. Box 11,
  Falmouth,
  Cornwall TR10 9EN.

Alternatively you may fax your order to the above address.
Fax No. 0326 376423.

Payments can be made as follows: cheque, postal order
(payable to Little, Brown and Company) or by credit cards,
Visa/Access. Do not send cash or currency. UK customers
and B.F.P.O. please allow £1.00 for postage and packing for
the first book, plus 50p for the second book, plus 30p for
each additional book up to a maximum charge of £3.00
(7 books plus).

Overseas customers including Ireland, please allow £2.00 for
the first book plus £1.00 for the second book, plus 50p for
each additional book.

NAME (Block Letters) ........................................................

................................................................................................

ADDRESS ........................................................................

................................................................................................

................................................................................................

☐ I enclose my remittance for _____

☐ I wish to pay by Access/Visa Card

Number ⬚⬚⬚⬚⬚⬚⬚⬚⬚⬚⬚⬚⬚⬚⬚⬚

Card Expiry Date ⬚⬚⬚⬚